SKUNKS
&
HOUND DOGS

D0042843

OTHER BOOKS BY ROBERT J. ADAMS

*   *   *

THE STUMP FARM

BEYOND THE STUMP FARM

HORSE COP

FISH COP

THE ELEPHANT'S TRUNK

THE SOUTH ROAD

SKUNKS

&

HOUND DOGS

ROBERT J. ADAMS

MEGAMY

THE PUBLISHER:
Megamy Publishing Ltd.
P. O. Box 3507
Spruce Grove, Alberta, Canada T7X 3A7
E-mail: megamy@compusmart.ab.ca

National Library of Canada Cataloguing in Publication Data
Adams, Robert J., 1938–
    Skunks and hound dogs
ISBN 0-9681916-9-X

    1. Adams, Robert J., 1938– — Anecdotes. 2. Outdoor
life--Alberta--Anecdotes. 3. Canadian wit and humor
(English) I. Title.

SK354.A33A3 2002   C818'.5402   C2002-901046-2

Senior Editor: Kelly Hymanyk
Copy Editor: Natalie King
Design, layout, and production: Kelly Hymanyk
Cover: NEXUS Design
Printing: Quality Color Press Inc

DEDICATION

For my brother Bruce,
whose life in this world was far too short.

DISCLAIMER

The stories you are about to read are all true. The men, women, and children you will read about are all people from my past. I have taken the liberty of changing the names of many of them to protect their identities. Although I view the past as being very humorous, they may not.

CONTENTS

ACKNOWLEDGEMENTS

I would like to thank Mar for her contribution to this book. Little did she or anyone else realize that the lifestyle demanded of the wife of a Fish and Wildlife officer would one day be central in many of my stories. Unbegrudgingly, she accepted the fact that, on very short notice, she would often be called on to provide meals and lodging for a brother officer. And more often than not, there was more than one officer who showed up at the door at the same time. For your excellent meals and great hospitality, Mar: I thank you, although those officers have said it on many occasions, once again, they thank you; and although it was never said, I'm sure the Division thanks you.

What can I say about George Freeman that many of the stories do not say. Thank you for all the great memories. For being an excellent mentor, a fabulous person, and the best of friends. There is no doubt, without you, many of these stories would not have occurred.

I have a special thanks to Natalie King for the great job of copy editing. And to Greg Dussome for our cover design.

A great big thanks to my daughter Kelly. Only, too well do I understand the effort that it takes to keep me focused, but she does, and she does it very well. I thank you for your insight and the excellent job of story editing. Kelly, you make the book.

INTRODUCTION

Since the beginning of time, storytelling has been a celebrated way to pass information from one group of people to the next, or from generation to generation. Long before television, radio, or newspapers people used storytelling to entertain or to disseminate the news.

How appropriate, then, that Adams uses his craft of storytelling to entertain readers, young and old, all the while presenting the history of the average Canadian. His stories are his own, but they belong to every man, woman, and child, because we all have a part in history.

Hats off to Adams for recording history with his charming, witty, style of storytelling. For getting his readers to remember to laugh at the little things in life, after all, that's what it's all about. Here's to you, Adams: thanks for the laughter, thanks for the memories.

MEGAMY PUBLISHING

SKUNKS
&
HOUND DOGS

"I'M GOING WHERE?"

"It's your mother," Mar said after answering the phone. "She wants to talk to you. She sounds like she's going to come right through the receiver. She's pretty excited."

And excited she was.

"Congratulations, Bobby!" Mom's voice bubbled into the receiver. "Isn't it great? I'll bet you're walking on cloud nine right now."

"Well, thank you, Mom," I replied cautiously. "And just what am I walking on cloud nine about?"

"Your promotion and transfer," she warbled on the other end of the line. "Aren't you excited?"

There was certainly no denying that I was excited about the possibility of a promotion and a transfer. In fact, that's all I had thought about since the Fish and Wildlife Division had advertised a competition for district officers during the winter and I had applied. To add to the excitement, there were twenty districts that were open for either a lateral transfer for Conservation Officers or a promotion for Assistant Conservation Officers. No matter how you cut it, sooner or later twenty Assistants were going to get promoted. And since I was currently an Assistant Conservation Officer, that sounded good to me.

When the competition came out, I had carefully reviewed each of the districts. Many of the district offices I knew only as the name of a town on a map, so I burned up the wires, making a number of calls, to ascertain the negatives and positives of each district. I talked to officers who had worked in one or more of the locations. I talked to many people who had lived, or knew of someone who lived, in one of the listed towns. I talked to the Powers That Be. I talked to anybody and everybody who would talk to me. I did my homework — I was not going to apply for any district without having garnered all of the information available. I would get plum in this pudding.

And it did not take long for the picture to clear. The best districts were those along the east slopes of the Rockies. Districts with mountains. These were the most desirable, and it filtered down from there. There were desirable districts, somewhat desirable districts, less desirable districts, and of course, totally unacceptable districts.

Two districts were earmarked as totally unacceptable for a young, ambitious Fish and Wildlife Officer. "Going to one of these districts is like being sent to the old folks' home," I was told. "There's nothing to do there. You'll go stir-crazy in a month. Leave the retirement districts for the old guys. You're too young to go there."

Armed with all this high-powered hearsay, knowledge, and information, I sat down with a map spread out in front of me. I ranked each and every district. Number one was followed by number two, and so it went down through the districts until I hit number twenty at the bottom of the list: Strathmore.

I had been with the Division for less than two years, but I was an ambitious young man. I was destined for great things and this was the opportunity of a lifetime. I submitted my application for promotion and transfer to the Powers That Be. I listed all the districts in order of priority, omitting districts ranked nineteen and twenty. Those I would leave for the old guys, the guys with one foot in the grave.

My future was in the hands of the Powers That Be. There was absolutely no doubt in my mind that I would be given one of the preferred mountain districts. It was my destiny. I had been anxiously awaiting the call from the Powers That Be, the decision-makers. But a phone call from my mother, who was four hundred miles away, congratulating me on something that hadn't been announced yet, was the furthest thing from my mind.

"Well, I think congratulations are in order," Mom blurted out, jogging me back to reality.

"Well, thanks." I replied.

"You don't sound happy," she observed, her voice sinking a notch.

"Oh yeah, Mom, I'm just busting with joy!" I laughed, humouring her. "You realize, I haven't heard anything about any promotion or transfer."

"You haven't?" she replied. "You're going to Strathmore!"

"I'm going where?" Suddenly I felt a pang in the pit of my stomach.

"Strathmore," she warbled again. "Oh, Bobby, I'm so happy for you. Aren't you excited?"

"Shocked, Mom," I mumbled. "I . . . I'm shocked. I don't know what to say."

"Oh, Bobby. And I thought you'd be so happy."

"W—with Strathmore?" I stuttered.

Then it suddenly hit me, and I started to laugh. "You know, that's a pretty good one, Mom. For a minute you almost had me believing that I did get a promotion and transfer. If you'd have said any place other than Strathmore, you'd have had me good. But Strathmore, that's impossible. I didn't bid on it." I smiled with relief. "Sorry to ruin your day, Mom."

"You mean you really haven't heard?"

"Nope, I haven't, not a peep from the Powers That Be," I replied. "Nothing on the moccasin telegraph either. But tell me, O bearer of not-so-great news, where did you get this little gem?"

"From the Fish and Wildlife secretary in Edson. She phoned to tell me."

My heart sank. The moccasin telegraph, the unofficial way to rapidly move information amongst the office staff by dropping a tidbit to the right person, was ninety-nine percent accurate most of the time.

News from the Fish and Wildlife secretary in Edson was one hundred percent accurate all of the time. It had to be true—this lady was connected. It was a well-known fact that you could bank on anything that she told you. I was Strathmore-bound.

Now, the new Strathmore District was not new at all. It was in fact the old Calgary East District. But the Powers That Be, in their ultimate wisdom, had decreed that the district and the city could be better served from a rural community. After all, it was pointed out, hunters and fishermen *left* the city to pursue their sports in the country. The words were ringing in my ears as Mar and I cruised down Highway 1 towards Strathmore and our new home.

"Bob, you'll be opening a brand-new office in Strathmore," the Powers That Be had said, trying to pump me up with encouraging words. "You should look at this transfer as the opportunity of a lifetime. You know, it's not everyone that we would trust with the onerous task of setting up a brand-new office. Just think, son, there's no baggage, there's no garbage to sort through. You'll be able to start fresh. You'll have new facilities. You can hire your own secretary. You'll be able to set up the office exactly as you want it to be. Yes, Adams, this is an opportunity of a lifetime. Take it and run with it, son."

There was no doubt the words were intended to help soften the blow, to cheer me up. After all, I was being promoted, and I would have my own office, my own district. I knew I should have been grateful, but it was downright difficult when deep inside I knew I was headed for the Old Folks' Home.

I certainly was not the happiest person in Strathmore as I drove into town the first day. Mar, however, was quite excited about the prospect of moving into a new house. She figured we had done our time in the basement suite in Brooks. First on the agenda was a house; after that we could check out the brand-new office. From researching the various districts, I had an idea that Strathmore was smaller than Brooks. I had explained this to Mar, but we were still surprised when it took less than five minutes to drive up and down the few streets and familiarize ourselves with the town.

"Did you see any houses for sale?" I asked Mar as we drove through town for the second time.

"No," she replied unhappily.

"What about an office?" I asked.

"I'm not looking for any office," she replied. "I want to know where I'm going to live." Mar wasn't really interested in my brand-new office building. However, when I drove down the main drag for the second time, I could not help myself, I peered into every window. Not one of those windows looked even remotely as if there might be an empty office behind it. They all resembled small-town retail outlets, and each outlet was open for business.

"Well, when all else fails, I guess it's best to talk to someone who knows," I said when a third trip through town failed to turn up either a house or an office.

"And who would that be?" Mar asked. "We don't know anybody here, do we?"

"Yeah, as a matter of fact, I do," I chuckled. "I know George Freeman."

George was the Ducks Unlimited representative in Strathmore. The boys in Brooks had told me that if I had any problems, just look George up; he knew everybody and everything that went on in Strathmore. So, ten minutes after I hit town, George was my man.

*   *   *

"I don't think so, boy," George laughed when I told him about my brand-new office. "I don't think there is an office here. As a matter of fact, I don't even think there's any available office space in town."

"What about a house?" asked Mar. "Are there any houses for sale or rent?"

"Not that I know of," replied George. "There's not too much of anything standing empty. How do you feel about living in a tent?" He laughed teasingly. I don't think that Mar found George's comment to be all that humorous.

"There's got to be an office," I said, and smiled at George. I was developing a fixation on that bloody office. I was also beginning to think that maybe George didn't know everything that went on in town. "The Powers That Be told me that I was opening up a brand-new office here," I added.

"Well, I can tell you one thing for sure," George said, laughing. "There is not a new office building in Strathmore. As a matter of fact, boy, there's no new building here period." We both laughed. My laugh was a pretty sick try at making the best of a rapidly deteriorating situation.

Another tour of the town followed. This time George drove, and he painstakingly pointed out every building. He knew the name of every business and every owner. He gave us the name of every occupant of every house, and in most cases, the history of the house as well. At the end of the tour, I had to admit there was no new office building. There was no house for sale or rent. I also knew what the boys in Brooks had told me was true: George did know everybody and everything that went on in Strathmore.

*   *   *

"I said, I can't find my office," I repeated into the phone. I was back in Brooks and talking to the Powers That Be.

"How did you like the town?" he asked for the second time, ignoring my comment.

"I like it worse now than when I left it off my application in the first place," I snarled. "I can't find my office, and that's only the half of it. There's not a house or a room for sale or rent either. And another thing, my wife is a legal secretary and there's not even a lawyer in Strathmore. She'll never find a job."

"How about the town?" he asked again, sounding like a stuck record. "Isn't it a beautiful little prairie town? You know, you're right on Calgary's doorstep. You'll be able to enjoy everything the city has to offer without having to put up with any of the city hassles."

18

"You told me I would have a brand-new office," I snapped, not letting him forget our earlier conversation.

But somewhere in our discussion he must have lost his patience.

"That's the problem with you young bucks," he snorted. "You want everything right now. You get a promotion and you whine that your wife can't find a job—"

"She can't find a house to buy or rent either," I snapped at him. But he was a master at avoiding the issue. My comment rolled off him like water off a duck's back.

"I promote you to a new district and you whine that you haven't got a new office. You'll get your office, Adams. All in good time. Just be patient. There's people looking right now; they'll find something."

"Not unless they're Houdini, or they're going to build," I replied dejectedly. "There's nothing vacant in town."

"Look Adams, it's a new district and things shouldn't be too busy for a while. "You can work out of your house for a while. Can't you?"

"No, I can't," I growled.

"And why not?" He sounded surprised.

"Because there are no bloody houses for rent there either. That's why!" I fumed and hung up the phone.

*   *   *

"You're in luck, boy, I think I've found you a house," came the cheerful voice over the phone. It was

19

George on the other end of the line. "There's a lady in town who has this big house. I think, if the right person came along, she might be willing to move into the basement and rent the top out. You should get down here as soon as you can, and we'll go visit her."

"I'm on my way!"

The house was a nice, modern, three-bedroom bungalow with a finished basement. The lady, Mrs. Rasmussen, wasn't really convinced that she wanted to rent any part of her house, let alone the upstairs, but she listened politely as George talked up a storm. I listened, too, for I knew there was nothing I could add about myself that would enhance what George was saying. In fact, I was wishing that the Powers That Be were there to hear what a marvellous person I was. Each time Mrs. Rasmussen said she wasn't sure, George talked faster. Before the afternoon was over, my new landlady was showing me which half of the garden was mine, and I was assuring her I would be only too happy to mow the lawn and trim the hedge.

Two months later, I had resigned myself to my fate—I was being put out to pasture long before my time. Reluctantly, I prepared for the move. But first, there were a few minor details to be ironed out. Once more, I phoned the Powers That Be.

"Where do I find all the equipment for this new office?" I asked.

"Let me see," he replied, "we've got you a typewriter, an adding machine, and a cash box. You can pick them up in Calgary."

"That's it?" I asked. "That's everything?"

"That's it," he replied. "What else do you need?"

"Well, I don't know. I suppose a couple of desks and some chairs. A counter and some filing cabinets, and some sort of filing baskets, and . . . and a wastepaper basket would be nice. I need a rifle, and a shotgun, and a boat and motor. I need a new pair of binoculars and—"

He cut me off before I could finish my list. "You don't have an office yet, Adams. You'll get the office furniture when you get an office. And the binoculars are personal inventory—take them with you. Take everything you've been issued with you."

"I don't want those old binoculars," I protested. "They're all I've been issued, and they don't work."

"That subject is closed," he stated. "Now is there anything else?"

"Yes, there is, the rest of my uniform and . . ., and another thing, now that I'm a Conservation Officer in charge of a district, I understand that I can use my own car and collect mileage, is that right?" I asked. Every other officer I knew who was in charge of a district was driving his personal car.

"You have to make an application for that privilege," he replied.

"Then I'm making an application, right now," I stated.

"Send me a memo and I'll personally see to it. Oh, and tell me, what kind of a car do you drive?" he asked.

"You know what kind of car I drive," I replied. "A 1960 red Volkswagen Beetle." There was a long eerie silence before he spoke again.

"Didn't we just send you a brand-new station wagon?"

"Yes," I replied, "but that's for the Assistant Officer in Brooks."

"You can take it with you," he said.

"No!" I groaned. "No, I don't want the station wagon. I want to go on private mileage like everybody else."

"Take the station wagon, Adams," he said firmly, "and you can make application for private mileage when you get yourself a real car."

With mixed emotions, we moved to the Old Folks' Home. Mar was elated; she had her house. No more basement suites—we were on the upper floor. I was downcast, not in the least impressed with my equipment: the Forestry Green station wagon, the wonky binoculars, two boxes of .303 shells, an old Underwood typewriter, a new adding machine, and a cash box. My uniform, or what I had of it, consisted of a box of pea-green ties, a flat-top forage cap without a hat badge, and a pair of shiny black leather oxfords. I had received a box of shirts with the name T. SMALL written on the box, and that's what they were, TOO SMALL. The neck was about a 12 and the sleeves no more than 27. Obviously, T. SMALL—whoever he was—had got my shirts, and he was probably walking around with the sleeves dragging on the ground. I returned the shirts, but T. SMALL must have had a bigger brother, because I still hadn't received a box of shirts with R. ADAMS written on it. And of course, I couldn't forget my latest acquisition: a pea jacket. A navy blue double-breasted overcoat made of coarse woollen cloth. These were traditionally worn by sailors, I was told, to protect them from the harsh wind and sea spray. It was somebody's idea of the ideal garment for summer on the Alberta prairie.

Unfortunately for me, those poor souls who were searching for office space had not been able to find any. But then, according to George, no one had yet made an appearance, or even asked about office space for Fish and Wildlife.

And so it came to pass that, through default, Mar's house also became my office. One of the small bedrooms became my storage room. It held the office supplies and exhibits. Martha's kitchen table was my desk. It held the only inventory the brand-new Strathmore District office had been issued — a typewriter and an adding machine. In a corner of the kitchen floor I stacked my stationery. Mar, too, contributed to the welfare of the Division, as her deep-freeze became storage for my perishable exhibits, should there come to be such things in the Old Folks' Home.

"Adams!" roared the voice on the other end of the telephone. "What do you think you're doing?" It was a little more than a month after setting up office that I received this unexpected call.

"Doing? Nothing that I'm aware of, why?" I replied honestly, because up to that time I had not found a thing to do. The Old Folks' Home was certainly living up to its reputation.

"I'm looking at your expense account," he snarled.

"And?" I asked.

"Since when do you think that the Division is going to pay for a private telephone?" he asked.

"Since the Division uses it more as their telephone than I do," I replied. "I thought it only fair that they pay at least half."

"I thought you were a bright young man," he said.

"How silly of me," I countered. "I must have had a weak moment to have even thought that fairness was something that would be considered."

"Long-distance calls," he informed me. "The Division will pay for any long-distance calls that you make. But remember, you'll have to justify each one."

"How much is the Division willing to pay for the rental of a storage room and the part of my kitchen I use for an office?" I asked.

Before he hung up the phone, it was abundantly clear to me that I should be thankful that I even had a job, let alone a district to work out of. My donation of the space and phone was a small price to pay.

Yes, indeed, I was very fortunate to be able to open a brand-new office. To be able to set it up exactly as I wanted it, or at least in the way which my wife would allow. And I was thankful that I could type, as my secretary would not arrive until some time after the new office. There was no doubt the Strathmore District would certainly bear my stamp.

I worked from my residence on the northern edge of town. Whenever they called, I would remind the Powers That Be that since coming to Strathmore, I had never, not even once, been late coming to work in the morning, nor did I leave the office early. But then, who was to know?

One of the best-kept secrets in the summer of '62 was the fact that a brand-new Fish and Wildlife office had opened in Strathmore, Alberta. That summer, the good folks who lived in that little prairie town twenty-four miles east of Calgary on the Trans-Canada Highway had, unbeknownst to them, been blessed. As they would come to learn, a Fish and Wildlife Officer, me, had unceremoniously been shipped into their midst.

It was a simple task to slip out of town at any time of the day or night, undetected. Like a shadow, I patrolled the district, up and down country roads and prairie trails, waving at the occasional farmer. I often noted the confused look on their faces as they returned the wave and searched their memory, trying to place the face in the Forestry Green station wagon. Heck, on occasion I even cruised through town undetected. For the Forestry Green station wagon was an unmarked vehicle.

Indeed, the brand-new Strathmore District sported a ghost car, a ghost office, and a ghost officer. No one could find them, even if anyone had wanted to. But then, no one knew they were there, so no one looked for them. Yes, the Division's secret, the best-kept secret during the summer of '62, was safe with me.

A WILDCAT IN THE SCHOOLYARD

It had been a long wait, but it was worth it, I thought, as I stood admiring myself in the latest parts of my uniform. For several weeks, months actually, various pieces of my uniform had been showing up. Some in the mail. Some hand-delivered. First came a box of ties, pea-green ties. Then I received a forage cap without a badge. A box of highly polished leather oxfords, of the type someone had dubbed "camel-kickers", was delivered. These I had brought with me from Brooks. And today, I received a tunic and two pairs of trousers, albeit heavy wool trousers, winter trousers. Except for the shirts and a hat badge, I now had an almost complete uniform.

I could not help but stand in front of the mirror and drink in the picture. Ah, yes, the Powers That Be would be proud, I thought, as I admired the cut of the tunic, how it fit broad through the shoulders and tapered narrow at the waist. And no one would ever miss the sharp crease that ran down both pant legs. Humbly, I had to admit that even without the shirts, I cut a fine picture in that uniform. Suddenly, my personal admiration was rudely interrupted.

"C'mon, boy, let's go!"George called, bursting through my front door. "There's a wildcat at the school."

George Freeman, Mr. Ducks Unlimited in southern Alberta and a long-time resident of Strathmore, was always enthusiastic, exuberant, and as I had learned, a willing participant in any adventure. On this day, his level of excitement was so great that his feet barely touched the floor as he bounced around my kitchen, and his voice was about four octaves higher than normal. Oh yeah, George was excited all right.

"You're sure it's a wildcat?" I asked cautiously as I peeled off the tunic, carefully put it on a hanger, and hung it in the closet. I didn't really share George's enthusiasm for charging into a schoolyard to capture a cat, whether it be a wildcat or a tame cat.

"Yes, boy, I'm sure!" he yelled excitedly. "There's a wildcat in the schoolyard in Carseland."

"How do you know it's a wildcat?" I asked.

"The principal, boy. The principal, he phoned me. He said, 'There's a wildcat in the schoolyard. Can you come and get rid of it?' He's concerned for the safety of the kids," George added, his enthusiasm not waning one iota.

"Well, I guess we better go and destroy it, then," I replied. "I might have to borrow your rifle, though," I added. George and I had often laughed about the equipment or lack thereof that I had been provided with, but he wasn't laughing now.

"Destroy it?" George replied, and his jaw dropped. Instantly, the enthusiasm and excitement were gone. George came back to earth, landing solidly on both feet. "Destroy it? No way, boy, I thought we'd just whip down there and catch it!"

"Catch it? Alive?" I replied, and a thousand thoughts flashed through my mind. Not the least of which was my wildcat-catching paraphernalia.

My brain was rapidly taking a mental inventory of equipment. Let's see now: Oh sure, I had a brand-new station wagon. That would take me to the scene, no problem there. And I had also received two more boxes of .303-calibre rifle shells. I had three boxes in total, but still no rifle to use them in. I could always *throw* them at any old wildcat. Of course, I still had the same old pair of wonky binoculars; these could also be thrown at a wildcat, or anything else for that matter. That was about the extent of the equipment I could muster for any attempt at capturing a wildcat. No, it was safe to say that I did not share any of George's excitement or enthusiasm. In fact, my feelings could best be described as dread, the fear of making an absolute fool of myself in front of a large group of people, mostly school-children.

"You're kidding me! Catch a wildcat?" I shivered at the very thought.

"Alive, boy," George confirmed. "We can catch it. C'mon, let's get going before it gets away. I've already phoned Tom Baines from the Calgary Zoo and he's going to meet us."

George's excitement and enthusiasm returned as quickly as it had disappeared. Once more he was bouncing around, his feet barely touching the floor.

I could only stand and stare at him. It was unbelievable that we would even contemplate catching a real live wildcat with two boxes of shells and a pair of wonky binoculars.

I knew deep down that it was not impossible that the wildcat could be a lynx. After all, I had been hearing rumours of lynx being seen in the area, and a larger-than-normal number of juveniles had shown up at the fur dealers during the past winter. This was the first report of a wildcat, and I suspected it would be a lynx. Since the reports began circulating, George and I had kidded about the possibility of catching a lynx alive. Obviously George's kidding had been just a tad more serious than mine. Even Tom Baines had made his wishes known.

"If you get the chance to catch a lynx, grab it. We'll take all the lynx that you can catch," said Tom. "Lynx are a valuable commodity. We can use a couple here for our display, and any extras we can always trade for animals which might otherwise not be available to us."

Waiting for Tom to arrive, we set about gathering all the equipment we would need for this adventure.

"We'll need a pole," I said. "A pole would be a useful tool to try and catch a wildcat. You got a pole?" I asked George. Ducks Unlimited had everything.

"Nope," he replied.

"Me neither. But don't worry, we can take an axe and cut a couple from someone's hedgerow," I said. George just looked at me.

"We don't need an axe," he replied happily. "I thought we could rope this cat. I've always wanted to try and rope a wildcat."

"Oh yeah, that sounds like real fun," I gave a sick little half-hearted laugh. "You ever try to rope a house cat?"

"It'll be fun," George replied assuringly.

"Yeah, well, I put a cord on a tame house cat one time. I learned my lesson real fast. It wasn't so tame. That thing opened its mouth and had teeth right back to its tail. That cat attacked and cut me to ribbons. My hands and arms looked like two pounds of ground round before I knew what was happening!" I shook my head at the very thought of a wildcat on the end of a rope. "Anyway, I don't got no rope either. My storage room is bare."

"I got a couple of pieces of rope," George replied. "We can make a couple of lariats. I'll bet one of us will be able to get a noose around that cat's neck."

Calgary Zoo to the rescue! Tom arrived with a metal cage, a short catch pole, and some more rope. All was not lost. I breathed a lot easier, knowing that we had proper equipment for our little safari. The three of us and Paddy, our trusted lynxhound, piled into George's car and, talking excitedly about catching wildcats, we sped off to Carseland. Just thinking about the upcoming ordeal made me sweat; I could probably wring a pint of sweat out of my shirt, I thought.

The fact that none of us had ever captured a live wildcat before didn't dampen the enthusiasm of my two partners; Tom was as excited as George. We had absolutely no idea what to expect. We were charging blindly into new territory, new adventure.

We didn't need Paddy our tracking hound to point out the wildcat's hiding place when we arrived at the schoolyard. Near the edge of the schoolyard were a few big old poplar trees. Every kid in the school, more than a hundred I'm sure, was gathered around the trunk of one of those poplars. High in the branches we could see a dark object. The wildcat had found the safest place in the country. It lay crouched on a large branch, thirty feet or more up the tree.

George drove over to the circle of kids and stopped his car. We got out and assessed the situation.

"It's a beautiful lynx," Tom said as he confirmed the identity of the wildcat.

There was a circus-like atmosphere around the base of that old poplar tree. The kids were all as excited as George was. They were screaming, and yelling, and laughing. Some were throwing rocks and sticks at the lynx. They wanted some action. If anyone other than myself was afraid of the lynx, it was not evident. Excitement? Yes, there was excitement in every rosy cheek. Adventure? You bet, there was a real sense of adventure in that schoolyard. Fear? No way, not one of those kids was afraid of anything. All the kids were there; they wouldn't have missed this show for the world. It was, after all, the best show in town. Come to think of it, it was the only show in town.

The lynx, meanwhile, was stretched out along the branch just looking down at the crowd. It showed no emotion, no excitement, no sense of adventure, and certainly no fear. The lynx appeared to be the calmest thing on the grounds.

After assessing the situation, we discussed our plan of attack, what would work best in this situation. Well, the kids' safety was the main concern. We certainly didn't want any of them to get hurt. The first thing to do, then, was to get the kids out of there and back in the classrooms, just in case something went wrong. I'm not sure why we thought "just in case something went wrong", when there was absolutely no reason in the world why anything should go right.

Being the man wearing most of a uniform and obviously someone in authority, it was my duty to move the kids and the teachers out of harm's way. And I tried, I really did, but my attempts to have the kids and the teachers move to the classroom or even away from the base of the tree was akin to trying to push a wet rope up a wall. Not one of those kids or teachers would move an inch. No one was going to miss any of the action. They stayed, clustered around the base of the tree, shouting and yelling at the top of their lungs. Carseland had not seen this much excitement in years.

Kids or not, it was finally time to get to work. Tom grabbed the metal cage. I got hold of the catch pole and George, still wanting to rope the lynx, made himself a lariat out of a length of rope. Armed to the teeth with our wildcat-catching paraphernalia, we waded into the circle of kids. It was not easy going. None of those kids wanted to give up their position and we, the three wildcat catchers, had to push our way into the throng and fight for a place at the base of the tree.

It was here, at the base of the tree, that reality set in. None of us had any experience in live-catching a lynx or any other wildcat, nor had we any idea as to how to go about it. Tom stood there with the metal cage, true, but had no idea how we would ever get the lynx into it. I had a catch pole that was about twenty feet too short to reach the branch that held the crouching lynx. And George—well, George held the lariat, but there was absolutely no way he could swing that thing through the maze of limbs between the ground and the lynx. We all stood there at the base of the tree and stared up while the lynx, crouching on his perch, stared down and watched the circus below.

It was obvious the lynx had settled in for the duration. He hadn't moved a muscle since we arrived.

"One of us can just shinny on up there and slip a rope over its head," George said as he eyed up the situation.

"Yeah, right. Then what?" I asked.

"Then we'll pull it out of the tree and stuff it into the cage," George replied.

"I don't know," I said cautiously. "I'm not too fussy about having a lynx on the end of any rope that I'm holdin' on to."

"We can get a forked branch," George suggested. "When he hits the ground, we'll just put the rope in the fork and run towards him and pin him to the ground, then we'll stuff him in the cage." It sounded pretty simple in theory, and it was the only solution we could think of.

Who would go up the tree with the lynx? Well, Tom was considerably older than George and I were; he also had a bad leg. George and I looked at each other. Yeah, I was the youngest and drew the short straw, I would go up the tree.

"You know, I think you'd look far more comfortable in any tree than I would," I mumbled to George as I prepared for the ascent.

I must admit that I was a tad overdressed for the occasion. My jeans and sneakers would have been more appropriate than my brand-new uniform trousers and my well-polished camel-kickers on that hot September day on the Alberta prairie.

I put my arms around the trunk of that old poplar tree and held on tight while I raised my knees to start shinnying up. A quick glance confirmed that the lynx was still on his branch and looking as unconcerned as ever. Even so, it's pretty darn hard to climb a poplar tree that has no limbs for the first fifteen feet or so, but to climb one with a lynx in it is an entirely different proposition. I found it very difficult to shinny up that tree with my head tilted back so that I could keep an eye on the lynx. It looked docile enough sitting there, but I had the horrible feeling that at any minute it would pounce, landing on my head. I could already feel the sabre-like claws raking my scalp.

It was a long, slow, agonizing ascent to the first branch. When I reached it I grabbed on first with one hand, then the other, and pulled myself up. I looked up again and the lynx looked down; his yellow eyes were staring a hole right through me. Now, there was no doubt, I had his attention. We were not that far apart and that docile lynx suddenly looked ferocious. At that moment, I knew I was the scaredest person in the schoolyard.

It was the lynx who made the first move. He raised his head, looked around, and then bared his teeth. This is it, I thought. This is where I meet my maker. Actually, I think he just yawned, but it was enough to make me hold my breath.

Then the lynx stood up on the branch. Realizing that I was not properly set to meet the charge of a lynx, I shifted my body and the camel-kickers took off—one went forward, the other backward, and I came within a whisker of falling out of the tree. I grabbed frantically for another branch, the tree trunk, anything. My hands were so sweaty that I could barely hold on to anything. My shirt was now soaking wet. And my trousers, my brand-new trousers that I had waited more than two years for, had not fared too well. White powdery stuff from the poplar had been ground into the new fabric, and a pant leg had paid a price for climbing a tree; a small nick of cloth hung down near my knee. My brand-new trousers were ruined.

I could have cried right there as I took stock of the damage, but my camel-kickers and their shiny, smooth leather soles chose that moment to take off again. The bark on that old poplar tree was as smooth as an ice surface and just as slippery. The kids in the schoolyard cheered wildly as I fought for my life. I frantically grabbed at branches, hoping to stay in the tree. This was not going to be fun.

As I struggled, the lynx just stared at me, then calmly used those sabre claws of his to hop up a couple more branches and settle down. I breathed a sigh of relief. Obviously, I thought, I had got closer than he liked. It was certainly closer than I wanted to be.

Suddenly I heard an excited voice — close, very close to me — say, "I can get up higher on them small limbs if you want me to."

I looked down, and there, clambering up the tree with all the agility of a monkey, was one of the kids. A young boy no more than ten years old, and he was right up in the tree with me and the lynx.

"What the — ? You . . . you shouldn't be up here," I snapped. "Get down right now! Do you understand?"

"It's okay, I'm a good tree climber," he warbled excitedly. "I can get right up there with that ol' wildcat. I'm not scared."

Well, maybe he wasn't scared, but I was, and I didn't need a kid up there with me. While we were arguing, he had shinnied right up until we were face to face in the tree. He wasn't about to back down for anything.

A voice from below yelled out, "Look out up there! He's moving again. The wildcat is moving."

The yelling and screaming increased as I glanced up and saw my worst fears about to come true. The lynx had just decided that enough was enough, that the old poplar tree was just getting too crowded. I realized that he wasn't going up or out on a limb — to my horror, he was coming straight at us, down the tree!

My first thought was that he might be attacking. I took a second look to see which one of us he was eyeballing. Who did he want to sink his sabres into first, me or the tender young kid? But there were no glaring eyes, no bared teeth. There was only fur. This didn't make sense, an attacking lynx coming at us butt-end-first, but that's exactly what he was doing. He was backing down the tree, coming right at us.

I looked at the kid, who was looking at the lynx. He might not have been afraid a couple of seconds earlier, but right now he was petrified and clinging to the tree for dear life. His eyes were about the size of saucers as he watched the lynx inching ever closer. The kid was smaller than me and he thought that he could get higher into the tree where the branches were smaller, but at that moment, we both had the same problem. The branches we were clinging to were solid enough where they grew from the trunk of the tree, but beyond that who knew? We had two alternatives: stay where we were, or fall out of the tree. We both braced to save ourselves and watched the furry end of the lynx come closer.

I held my breath as the stubby tail came level with my eyes and slowly drifted past. The kid, whose eyes were still about the size of saucers, disappeared from my sight as the long, grey, furry body passed between us, following the tail down the tree. A lifetime passed before the shoulders and neck came even with my face, and then suddenly there was the head, with those large yellow eyes. We were only inches apart, and I was looking the lynx right in the eye, I thought I might fill my drawers. Then he turned to look at the kid who, like myself, was still frozen, clinging to the tree.

My worst fears were being realized. This was not a fun trip. My heart was pumping wildly as the lynx inched his way past us. I could clearly see and hear those wicked sabre claws digging into the bark of the tree. They looked to be about an inch long, maybe longer, as they were slowly retracted from one hold and inserted into the next. Now I prayed that those claws would keep on going to find the solid base of the tree and not a part of my body.

The lynx picked his way down the trunk of the tree, having quite skilfully avoided both the kid and myself. I for one was breathing much easier than I had been a few seconds earlier. The kid in the tree with me was going absolutely crazy, shouting and yelling as if he had just conquered the world. He was not just happy with his part in the whole process — he was ecstatic. He was letting the world know that he had just stared down a wildcat and lived to tell the tale. He would be a classroom hero for many days to come. The kids on the ground cheered with him.

The lynx continued its gradual descent to within a few feet of the ground, then leapt from the tree, twisted in the air, and landed on all fours. Feeling much more secure, in my lofty perch, I watched as he stood facing the ring of onlookers. The kids were deathly silent. The lynx took a tentative step towards the group. A child moved to one side and the lynx moved forward. Another child moved, then another. I had the best seat in the house, and I marvelled at how calmly that lynx

38

picked its way through the ring of kids. Those closest to the lynx tried to back away, those at the back pushed forward for a better look. Many a child could easily have reached out and touched the lynx as he passed by. The lynx was not interested in doing anyone any bodily harm; he only wanted to be get away from the crowd.

Once free of the circle of kids, the lynx broke stride and loped towards another poplar tree about a hundred yards away, climbed out of harm's way again, and settled down on a nice comfy branch. There it sat, waiting for me and for the next series of events to unfold.

The kids did not hesitate for one second. They bolted after it, hollering and throwing things. The kid who had joined me in the tree left it as easily as if he had been born in one. He dropped to the ground and raced after his schoolmates. I was not so graceful, and in what could be described as little more than a semi-controlled fall, I plummeted to the ground. I didn't race after the lynx, for I knew what awaited me at the next tree.

I stood alone under my tree and took stock. My nice shiny, slippery, leather-soled shoes were all scuffed and scraped. The shine had been left behind on the bark of the poplar tree, and chunks of leather had been gouged out. And now I knew that heavy woollen pants were not really meant for a hot prairie day. My legs were boiling hot and sweaty, and there was no longer a crease right down the pant legs. The small nick on the knee had become a large tear. Actually, now that I had the opportunity to look at the pants, I noticed little nicks all over them, and stray threads stuck out like unkempt hair. This lynx caper was exacting a heavy toll. At best, my brand-new trousers would have to be dry cleaned, and I paid for that. At worst and most probable, they would be ready for the ragbag. The Powers That Be would not be impressed. I had escaped injury in the first go-round, but I was not at all confident that my luck would hold, I expected that sooner or later that lynx would exact a little satisfaction with a good measure of my hide.

I walked slowly towards my wildcat-catching buddies and the swarm of howling, squealing kids. There was no rush. I had to climb another tree and I knew that lynx would wait for me.

"How come you didn't catch it when I sent it down to you?" I asked George and Tom as I arrived at the tree. "Didn't you notice how I got him to slowly back down? He would have backed right into the cage if you'd held it there. What's the matter with you two?"

George laughed. "You just get a rope on it and we'll get it in the cage."

"Yeah, well, they tell me good help's really hard to get. Now I know what they mean," I countered, delaying the inevitable.

Up another tree I shinnied. The bark exacted another measure of revenge on my uniform pants and collected what remained of the shoe polish on my shiny, slippery shoes. I was carefully inching my way up towards the lynx. If it was possible, I was moving even more slowly than last time. The lynx didn't move; he crouched on his perch and watched me intently as I got closer. I was alone in the tree with the lynx, as the kid had stayed on the ground, lost in the crowd.

The lynx, looking over his shoulder, watched my every move. Not once did he take his unblinking eyes off me. I was able to get within a few of feet of my target, but not close enough to use the catch pole. So far so good, I thought, as I looked at the butt end of the lynx, the closest part of his anatomy to me. With the aid of a forked stick that my partners had passed to me, I moved to try and get the noose over his head. I certainly had a very patient subject. I fiddled around, trying to maintain my balance and a hold on the tree. I hooked the noose over the forked stick, and with one hand I nervously tried to manoeuvre the noose over the head. But the lynx simply moved his head to one side or the other, and all the while he kept an eye on me.

"Make sure you get one leg in the noose, as well as his head!" Tom shouted directions from below. Tom was the expert on handling live animals; he knew what should be done. Doing it up a tree without proper equipment, though, was something else. "We don't want to strangle him, and that's what will happen if the rope's just around his neck," he cautioned several times.

"Yeah, well, I'm having enough trouble just trying to get the bloody rope around its neck without worrying about a leg, too," I grumbled. Sweat was streaming down my face, and the ruddy uniform pants were like an oven.

"You'll have to make sure that you get one leg in the noose or we'll have a dead lynx," Tom repeated from the safety of the ground.

"I'm having enough trouble getting *any* part of him in the noose," I snapped again.

"Don't be afraid to get a little closer if you have to," George said encouragingly.

"Yeah, we want a little action. Get closer!" cheered a chorus of ecstatic kids.

"Sure, that's all I need is to get a little closer. I'm just about sitting on the bloody thing as it is," I grumbled as the cat dodged the noose for the umpteenth time.

"At the rate you're going, it'll be dark and we won't be any farther ahead," George volunteered.

"Look, if I'm not doing this right, one of you can come up here and show me the proper way. You certainly won't hurt my feelings none."

Man, that is a patient animal, I thought as I smacked it on the side of the head with the rope — this, of course, after I had already scraped the rope over the top of its head, along its neck, and across its back. Finally, through absolutely no fault of mine, the noose slipped over its head and around its neck. The lynx was unbelievably calm. It just sat there, looking back at me, with the rope hanging around its neck.

"Hey, you got him, Bob!" shouted Tom, and the crowd of kids all cheered. "That's good, now you just have to get one foot through the loop, then you've got it made," Tom called encouragingly.

"How d'you expect me to do that?" I asked. "Please lynx, lift your foot so's I can get you cinched up real good?"

"Well, you've got that stick, and maybe you can work the noose under one foot. Just hang in there.

You'll get it, you're almost there now," Tom replied.

With the stick I tried to get the lower part of the noose out and over one leg. Both legs were pretty close together on the branch, and the lynx was not co-operating. There was no way he would spread his legs to accommodate me.

"What if I get both legs? I don't think I'm going to be able to get the rope in between them."

"That's no good," Tom answered. "You'll never be able to handle him if the rope's around his middle. Next to choking him, that's the worst place it could be."

The forked stick was slimy and wet from sweat as I tried to force the rope between his front legs. Then, the unthinkable happened. The noose slipped off his neck. The rope fell down along the tree trunk and dangled useless in my hand.

"Got any more bright ideas?" I asked. "That last one was a doozy."

Now I was back trying to get the noose around the neck. The lynx was just as patient as ever, sitting there and waiting for his fate—which, at the rate we were going, could well be to sit on that limb for the rest of his natural life.

"I don't know, Tom, I got the loop around his neck again, but the way he's sitting on them legs of his, it'll be tough to get the rope under one of them," I called down.

"You gotta get one leg in the noose. It's the only way we can be sure of keeping him alive," Tom insisted. "We don't want to kill him."

I was trying very diligently to get a portion of the

rope under one leg when the lynx finally decided he'd had enough. He'd had it with all the harassment and his front paws being constantly poked and jabbed with a forked stick. He stood.

"Now's your chance. Get the rope under one foot while he's standing," came the encouraging words from below.

At that moment, I was stretched right out, leaning towards the moving lynx with the forked stick in my hand, trying to get the rope under one leg. Besides trying to get the rope in position, which was becoming less of a priority every second, I was hanging on to the tree for dear life with one hand. I'm sure my toes were curled around the branch I was standing on, right through my camel-kickers.

When the lynx stood up, he had pulled up a fair amount of the slack in the rope and the noose around his neck had tightened. There was no paw in it, head and neck only. The lynx casually made a leap for another branch just a little higher up the tree, and a moment later the rodeo was on.

Getting one leg in the noose suddenly become the least of my priorities. The lynx was airborne when he hit the end of the rope. The noose snugged right up tight around its neck, and I felt the rope jerk in my hand. It was strictly reflex that caused me to tighten my grip on both the rope and the tree. I grasped both as tight as I could.

Instantly, I had two problems: In one hand I had a thrashing, flailing, choking lynx. In the other I had a limb that I prayed was strong enough to hold me, for my camel-kickers chose that moment to leave the branch. They both shot off in different directions. I was in as dangerous a situation as the lynx.

With one hand I held on to a branch above my head; with the other I held the rope with a lynx dangling from the other end, clawing and scratching. I was kicking my feet around, frantically trying to find the branch they had just left. Whenever I did manage to make contact with the branch, the slippery soles would find another way to leave. Like a trooper, I fought gallantly to remain in the tree and to keep a hold on the rope and the lynx.

But the calm, cool, collected lynx had also received a major surprise. The dreaded choke hold was on. The momentum of the jump carried the animal away from the tree and me. The startled cat had fallen over the wrong side of the limb he had been sitting on, and when he reached the end of the rope, he was suspended in mid-air above the cheering crowd, flailing wildly. Claws like sabres flashed in the sun as they reached for anything to grab hold of.

I still had the rope in my hand and had just managed to get one foot on a branch when the rope jerked again. The camel-kicker responded immediately, and for the second time I went through another bout of fancy footwork to stay aloft.

"Be careful!" someone yelled from below.

"I'll be okay as soon as I get my balance," I shouted back. "These shoes are pretty darn slippery on this poplar limb."

"No, not you, for cripes sake! The wildcat! Be careful

with the wildcat. You're killing him. Let him down. Let him down!"

Reality again. They weren't concerned about me at all. Here I was, risking life and limb, and they were only concerned about the animal.

"What do you want me to do, drop him?" I snapped.

I wasn't at all convinced that I could keep myself from crashing to the ground, let alone the lynx, and now that I had him, I didn't want to lose him and have to go through this effort again.

"Lower the rope, you dummy!" someone yelled at me again. "You're choking him to death. Let him down."

Sure, now everyone's an expert, I thought to myself.

"How d'you expect me to do that?" I yelled back. "I've only got two hands, and I'm using both right now."

The lynx continued to flail away, while I struggled to stay in the tree and hang on to the rope. Finally, I got my feet settled and into a position where I could use both hands to lower the lynx towards the waiting cage.

Getting this lynx into the cage would be no small feat. He was all legs and claws as he neared the ground, swinging those claws at anything that got close. Neither of my partners wanted to venture too close to the menacing claws. However, the fight was slowly being choked out of him. Soon those long legs no longer flailed wildly. His thrashing was becoming more feeble, and the ground party was finally able to get the cage under him. I lowered a fairly limp lynx into the cage.

Happily, I dropped the rope and used both hands to

cling to the tree. From my perch high above the schoolyard, with my camel-kickers firmly planted on a large branch, I watched the circus in relative safety. Tom was the first to act. The lynx had barely hit the bottom of the cage when Tom dove right in with both hands. It seemed like his arms, his head, and his neck were in the cage with the lynx as he took the noose off the animal's neck.

The circus atmosphere echoed across the schoolyard as screaming, yelling, cheering kids all pushed and shoved to have a look at the caged lynx. George grabbed the cage and bolted for his car. Every kid on the schoolyard charged after him. Somehow, he was able to get the cage into the trunk as the howling mob gathered around for another look at the caged wildcat.

I was amazed that I was still alive. I looked around. Now, I thought, if only my knees will stop knocking and I can pry my fingers off these branches, I'm sure that, with the help of my camel-kickers, I will be able to fall out of this old poplar tree.

Back home in Strathmore, I took a personal inventory. I had lost the sharp crease in my recently-new trousers. I had acquired snags, rips, and tears that were beyond repair. It would now be impossible to get a spit shine on my brand-new camel-kickers, scraped and gouged as they were. But I, with my trusty sidekicks, had rid the schoolyard of danger, kept the lynx alive, and managed to help out the Calgary Zoo. Not bad for a kid from the Stump Farm.

Once again, I admired myself in front of the mirror. I was a mess, but I was a proud mess.

AN EARLY DUCK SEASON

After several months in the Strathmore district, I was beginning to think that it was indeed the "Old Folks' Home" of the Alberta Fish and Wildlife districts.

Once the boys I worked with in Brooks found out that I was going to Strathmore, they never wasted an opportunity to kid me about my promotion and posting.

"I always thought you were a young fellow with a lot of ambition," Fred would say and shake his head sadly. "But in the blink of an eye, you jump at the chance to go to the Old Folks' Home."

"They sent me there," I reminded him.

"Just when you think you know someone . . .," he said, with mock disappointment ignoring my comment. "You know, Bob, there's never been a ticket written in the Strathmore District."

"So you've told me, at every opportunity," I grumbled. Yeah, the kidding and ribbing stopped only after I moved to Strathmore, the Old Folks' Home.

Those comments had never left my mind. And this Saturday morning was no exception, as I sat on my back steps and contemplated my fate. I would have given my left arm to be sitting in one of the mountain districts getting ready for a day in the rocks. Instead, I was looking forward to another hot, dusty day on the Alberta prairie. It was a little after six on this morning and the sun shone brightly on my back steps, warming me.

The Powers That Be had not treated me well this past year, I lamented, for I truly believed that I deserved a better fate, or at least a better district where something — anything — happened once in a while.

Before walking out onto the steps, I had polished off a healthy heaping of bacon, eggs, toast, and coffee. It was a hearty meal for a condemned man, condemned to spend another day patrolling the back roads, alone, for that is what I had been doing since I arrived in Strathmore. The guys had been right, it was the Old Folks' Home.

POP. POP. POP. The sounds, so sudden and quick, startled me.

"What the —," I mumbled as I turned towards the direction of the noise.

POP . . . POP.

Well, I'll be, I thought to myself. Those pops that sounded a little like firecrackers were, to the trained ear, the sounds of a shotgun being fired. And they're not

49

that far from here. The duck season wouldn't open for a week yet, and I hadn't issued any damage permits this close to town. I would have thought that on a nice morning like this, the farmers would be busy getting in their harvest. They usually didn't worry about the ducks unless it was rainy and wet and they couldn't get into the fields.

"Could this be? Could . . . could someone actually be poaching in the realm of the "Old Folks' Home?" I asked myself.

I raced for the Forestry Green station wagon. This wasn't what I had had in mind on this fine morning, but being a very curious fellow I decided to go and have a look-see. Actually, I was dying to get out there.

I headed north out of town, in the direction of the shots. In my haste I almost missed the two individuals walking along one of the irrigation canals that was only about four hundred yards from my house. Even without using my wonky binoculars, I could tell they were each carrying firearms. And lo and behold, I could also see ducks. Both carried ducks in their free hands. I waited at the road, beside the car, as the pair ambled towards me along the canal bank. They strolled along, laughing and chatting, just like they were in their right minds.

I greeted them when they reached their car. "Morning, fellas. How's the huntin' this time of year?"

"Great!" replied one of the hunters.

"Yeah, like they say, the early bird gets the worm!" warbled the second.

"Really! Don't you think it's a little early, even for

50

the worm?" I asked.

"We like to get out here before the competition," the first guy said, and gave me a great big belly laugh.

"Yeah, I'd say coming out about a week before the season opens would narrow the competition considerably," I replied.

"Hey, that's a good one!" And they both laughed.

Man, these guys were so relaxed I was beginning to have second thoughts. Maybe I was wrong. Had I been lulled to sleep in the Old Folks' Home, had the season actually opened this morning? Had I misread the *Synopsis?* Or maybe it was me, my appearance. These guys obviously didn't recognize me as a Fish and Wildlife officer. I looked down to check myself over. Had I left something off when I got dressed this morning? I checked my issue trousers. A couple of weeks ago they had been brand new, but now both knees had ugly patches on them — my badges of honour, the result of climbing a tree to catch a lynx, the only action thus far in the Old Folks' Home. Today, for the first time, I even had an almost-issue shirt on; it was one that I had been able to keep when I left the RCMP. The outlines of the RCMP shoulder flashes were still there, but they didn't show under the tunic. And the pea-green tie was hanging around my neck. I reached up and checked it, sure enough, the knot was there, the tie was in order. And my tunic, at this point the pride of my uniform, was still brand new, not a mark on it. Surely the shiny brass buttons and the bright green and yellow shoulder flashes on the tunic were visible to these two nimrods.

POP . . . POP. POP . . . POP.

Another volley of shots rang out to the north of me. I stopped and looked in that direction in time to see a flock of ducks flare away from a small pond. Now, for sure, I knew it wasn't my appearance. There were more hunters, the season had to be open. Man, does an old folks' home ever have an effect on a person, I thought — I just about slept right through the opening of duck season.

"Do you fellas have your hunting licences?" I asked.

"You bet we have!" laughed the first guy. "You don't think we'd be dumb enough to go hunting without a licence, do you?"

"You never know," I replied. "Stranger things have happened. How about a hunting synopsis? Either of you got a *Synopsis* with you?"

"Right here in the car," replied the first hunter again.

"Would you like to get it and read the part about the opening date for duck season in this zone?" I asked.

I knew that one of us would be feeling a little silly in a couple of minutes.

"What's the matter, they didn't teach you to read at game-warden school?" he said.

"Something like that," I replied.

They both laughed as the first hunter pulled a bag from the car and took out his hunting synopsis. He made a big deal of unfolding the document and spreading it out on the hood of the car. He rubbed his open palms over it, smoothing out the folds.

"I've been asked for my licence many times, but I have to admit, I've never been asked to tell the game warden when the season opens," he said shaking his head.

"It's the latest thing," I replied. "In fact, they teach it now at game-warden school."

"Are you serious? I didn't know that they sent game wardens to school," he responded with a funny little look.

"They don't," I assured him.

"Yeah, that's what I thought. Okay now . . . now you bear with me, partner. You know I've never been asked to do this before," he said playing at being serious as he leaned over the hood of the car. He studied the *Synopsis* for a few seconds. "Okay, let's see now, uh, today is Saturday the . . .," and then he paused. "Well, I'll be darned! Would you look at that!" he said to his partner.

"What's that?" asked his partner.

"The duck season . . .," he said slowly, "it says here the duck season doesn't open until next week."

"Yeah, now that is something, isn't it," I declared, and breathed a sigh of relief. "You know, fellas, that's the way they *would have* taught me at game-warden school to read it, too."

"Well now, if that just doesn't beat all. You know we're really sorry," said the second hunter, not missing a beat. "We promise you, Officer, we sure won't do this again. Will we?" he asked his partner.

"No sir, you can count on that. We won't do this again," echoed the first hunter. Both men were smiling. Hunting out of season and getting caught, so what? Obviously it was no big deal. "Oh, and I want to thank you for bringing it to our attention," he added as an afterthought.

I still couldn't believe how calm these two were. It was as though this sort of thing happened every day. They were so unconcerned about what was going to happen to them now that they were caught.

"Well, fellas, you're right about one thing," I said and smiled back at them.

"What's that?" asked the first guy.

"You certainly won't be doing it again, not with these shotguns anyway, because I'm going to have to take them both for evidence, along with the ducks, of course, and in return I'll just give you a little ticket to appear in court. You'll both be charged with hunting ducks out of season."

"What?" they both howled in unison. They stood there in total disbelief as I relieved them of the firearms and the ducks. Gone were the smiles and nonchalant, carefree attitude as soon as I handed them each a ticket and a receipt for the seizures.

POP. POP.

Once again I heard the sound of shots, coming from the north. It appeared that there was life within the confines of the Old Folks' Home after all.

They both gave me the funniest look as I placed their shotguns on the back seat and their ducks in the back of the Forestry Green station wagon. "Sorry, fellas, I'd like to stay and chat," I said, "but I hear another shotgun calling me."

On a Ducks Unlimited project a few miles northwest of Strathmore I found a car parked on the edge of a field. I hauled out my wonky binoculars and glassed a series of small ponds. At the edge of one, I thought I detected something. One of the blurry dark blobs in a patch of bulrushes seemed to move. Now fully confident, dressed in my uniform, I strode out to investigate. As it turned out, there was not one, but three dark blobs. All three were hunters, and all three were quite upset that I had the audacity to spoil their hunt by walking in on them.

"Get down or get your sorry butt out of here, you blankety-blank-blank idiot," one of them roared at me. Then one of them stood up and waved his arm for me to retreat. "Get out of here, you're scaring our ducks!"

Once they realized that I was not intimidated and was not to be scared away by a lot of waving and roaring, complete with a string of curse words as long as my arm, they relaxed. When I arrived at the edge of the pond, they greeted me like an old long-lost friend. As soon as they were reminded that the duck season was not open, these three also showed remorse for opening the season a week early.

"Officer, I can assure you that we will not do this again," one of the hunters vowed. "You know," he added, "I just don't understand how we could have made such a mistake."

POP. POP . . . POP.

There were more shots in the distance. This time it was a volley to the east.

I escorted the threesome back to my Forestry Green station wagon. To say that they were surprised when I relieved them of their shotguns and ducks would be an understatement. They were absolutely stunned by the chain of events. They stood with heads bowed as I carefully explained the legal process to them and advised them of their date with the court system.

Before I had a chance to depart, another vehicle came into view, crawling towards us along the peaceful country road. I stepped out to the centre of the road and waited for them. The vehicle inched along. The occupants paid absolutely no attention to me; their eyes and thoughts were on other matters as they scanned the ditch for any sign of birds. I waved to the driver to pull over and stop.

"Hey guys, look, it's the game warden," yodelled the driver as he stepped from the vehicle. Four guys inside the car laughed at the comment.

One of them shouted, "Hi, game warden!"

Obviously this was some sort of joke, for it was followed by a round of hilarious laughter.

"I don't think you're going to find this that funny." It was a serious comment that came from one of the three I had just dealt with.

"Is that so?" said the driver and chuckled. This crew still found it humorous that they had been stopped.

"Good day, gentlemen," I greeted them. "How's the hunting today?"

"Hunting?" replied the driver. "Who's hunting? Are we hunting, boys?" he called to his partners.

"No! We're not hunting!" came the boisterous reply.

"You're not hunting," I echoed. "Well, you guys sure fooled me. You know, the last time I saw a group of men all carrying shotguns and dressed in bird-hunting clothes, they were bird hunters. I would have sworn that you were bird hunters too. That just goes to show, you can't always believe everything you see."

"We just came out for a leisurely drive in the country," replied the smiling driver.

"Well, you've certainly picked a nice day for it," I replied. "And since you're here and I'm here, I suppose I might just as well have a look at those shotguns."

"What do you mean, look at our shotguns?" He paused and looked at his buddies still sitting in the car. "You . . . you mean you're gonna check our guns? But we ain't hunting!"

"That's okay. You don't have to be hunting to have your guns checked," I assured him. Needless to say, having their guns checked was a new experience. The five, out for a leisurely drive in the country, were very surprised. But not nearly as surprised as when I found two of the guns were loaded.

"Would you look at this! Live shells right down the spout. Now, this is not a very good start for a drive in the country, gentlemen," I said shaking my head.

"Well, thanks for bringing that to our attention," one of the occupants blurted out. "We'll make sure that all the guns are unloaded in the future."

"I'm sure you will. In fact, I'm counting on it," I replied.

"Right," he said, "you can certainly count on it."

"Now, what about your trunk?" I asked. "While I'm at it, I might as well take a look in your trunk. I don't suppose that you'd have anything in the trunk that would interest me, would you?"

"Nothing. The trunk's empty," replied the driver. "Like I said, we haven't done any hunting."

"Well, since I'm already here, why don't I take a look anyway," I said and walked around to the back of the car.

"You can't look in there," replied the driver. "Anyway, I don't have a key for it."

"You know, I think maybe there is something in there. And it looks like whoever put it in there must have dragged it in when you weren't looking. Here, look at this," I said and pointed to a smear of blood that graced the bumper and the back of the trunk. "This really doesn't look good. I guess you have a choice, my friend — you can open it, or I will."

"I don't have a key," he repeated and shrugged his shoulders.

"Neither do I, but I suppose that I can always use one of the shotguns," I said.

"You . . . you wouldn't?" For the first time, he was sober.

"Oh yeah, I would," I assured him. "In fact, that's something else *you* can count on."

"No! That's okay. I'll open it," he responded quickly, and just as quickly he produced the key he did not have. Inside the trunk, about a dozen ducks lay scattered on the floor.

"Not a bad haul for a leisurely drive in the country," I declared as I sorted and counted the birds.

"Okay. Okay, so we shot a few ducks. I'm sorry, I know I should have been more honest with you. But don't you worry, we won't shoot any more." He smiled.

58

"Oh, I'm not worried. I know you'll keep your word," I said as I took their shotguns and ducks and added them to my collection.

Mar wasn't even out of bed when I carried the first armload of shotguns into the back bedroom — or as I referred to it, the Strathmore District exhibit room. It was probably a good thing, for she would not have been impressed when I commandeered a portion of her deep-freeze for the perishable exhibits. I made several trips into the basement, carrying ducks, and still had one more trip to make when I heard the unmistakable sound.

POP . . . POP. POP

It was another volley of shots to the north of town. I hurried to get the last of the ducks out of the vehicle and into our freezer, then I raced away towards the sound of the shots.

And so it went for the rest of the day. I followed gunshots until dark. I travelled north, and east, and south, and west. I drove from one Ducks Unlimited project to the next, from irrigation canal to irrigation canal, from Strathmore to Beiseker. I zigzagged back and forth across the country checking early-season duck hunters. I made several flying return trips over rough dusty back roads to the Strathmore office — or as Mar lovingly called it, home — to store shotguns and ducks.

The sun had long since set in the west by the time I made my final trip to Strathmore.

Poor Mar, nothing could have prepared her for what happened to her home on that fateful day. Oh, she had got used to being the wife of a Fish Cop. She was raised on a farm in Saskatchewan and understood that when there was work to be done, you stayed until it was finished. Being a game warden in the early 1960s was no different. My supper was always ready, and more often than not, it was being kept warm in the oven. She was also used to the many strays that arrived at our door. There had been deer and antelope fawns. There had been a baby beaver. There had been Western grebes. And there had been a multitude of baby ducks that swam happily about the bathtub. But she was not prepared for what I brought home that day.

"Holy! What are all those guns for?" she asked as I hauled the last armload of shotguns through the back door, through her kitchen, down the hall, and into the spare bedroom, also known as the exhibit room.

"Seizures," I replied happily. "Every last one of them is a seizure."

"How many are there?"

There's lots of 'em," I said grinning from ear to ear. "I don't know how many, but there's lots. I'll count them later."

"Well . . . well, what are you going to do with them?"

"Keep them in the back bedroom," I replied.

"For how long?" she asked. "I don't want all those guns in my house."

"For as long as it takes, I guess," I muttered. "At least till I get my new office."

But if Mar was surprised at the number of shotguns that were hauled through her kitchen, that was nothing compared to her response when she opened the lid of her deep-freeze. I had tried to keep her items separate, but it was impossible. There were ducks, fully feathered ducks, piled to the top. Somewhere, down under that pile of feathered exhibits, were Mar's groceries.

"What am I supposed to do with all them stupid ducks?" she asked.

"I have to keep them at least until the court case is finished," I replied.

"How long will that be?"

"I don't know. A month, maybe more," I replied. "I have to keep them for thirty days after court, for the appeal period."

"I think you better find a different place for them. I need my deep-freeze for my stuff."

"Yeah, I know," I mumbled. "But there's no place else that I can take them."

Although the ducks in the deep-freeze and the shotguns in the spare bedroom did nothing to endear Mar to my working out of the house, the inconveniences came with the territory. I could only marvel at how accommodating the wife of a game warden had to be.

When I finished supper, I set about the task of preparing the court documents. I had set court for a week from Monday and had to ensure that each case was ready. For each ticket that I had written, I had to type out an Information, which contained the name and address of the individual, the date of the alleged violation, and the wording of the actual violation. There were four copies of each charge, and each had to have a piece of carbon paper. In order to make sure that the last copy could be read, one had to virtually hammer on the typewriter keys. There were also affidavits of seizures and exhibit reports to be prepared. They, too, had multiple copies and carbon paper.

I pounded on the typewriter all day Sunday, Monday, Tuesday, Wednesday, Thursday, and Friday. I pounded on it before breakfast, all morning and afternoon, and I pounded on it every evening and long into the night. It took me six full days to complete the paperwork. When it was all complete, my fingers were sore. I had an ache that started in the lower part of my back and shot up along my spine to my neck. From there it took a jagged course, like a bolt of lightening, through my skull to my eyeballs, where I had the worst headache imaginable. But nothing could dampen my spirits. I was elated—I had written seventy-six tickets.

The legend of the Old Folks' Home had been put to rest.

THE MILO OFFICE

It was just past noon when I arrived at the little town of Milo, in southern Alberta. I was to meet one of the Senior Officers and assist him in the upcoming commercial fishery.

"I'll be at the hotel," he had informed me when I spoke to him on the telephone.

Finding the hotel was no problem. It was a two-storey building, and the only one in town with vehicles around it. There were trucks of every description — half-ton trucks, three-quarter-ton trucks, trucks with stock racks, trucks without stock racks, and there were even a couple of cattle liners. If the trucks were any indication and the Powers That Be were correct, the commercial fishery on the lake was a big winter event.

I found a place to park about a block away from the hotel. I stepped out of my Forestry Green station wagon and brushed off my trousers. Then I tugged at my tunic to make sure that it lay properly. I placed my fur hat on my head at just the right angle. There, I thought, now I'm ready. I'm ready for all comers. With all the confidence in the world, I strode into the lobby of the Milo Hotel and rang the bell for the clerk.

"Can I help?" a voice called from up above. I looked up. Just my luck, I thought, I got the maid.

"I'm looking for the Fish and Wildlife Officer," I asked the lady who was standing at the top of the stairs holding a mop. "You wouldn't happen to know where I could find him?"

"He's in his office," she stated in a manner that suggested anyone with half a brain would look in his office.

"Office?" I repeated. Just the mention of the word office was enough to gall me. Immediately, I was ticked off, and inside my spiffy uniform I could feel the temperature rising. What really riled me was the fact that the Division didn't even have an officer stationed in Milo, and now I was being informed, by the hotel maid no less, that there was an office here. Meanwhile, back in Strathmore I was still working out of my house. Someone was going to get an earful when I got back home.

The maid never said a word, but the look said it all: "What kind of a dummy have they sent here this time?"

In a voice that I hoped would not disappoint her, I asked what probably seemed to be a redundant question.

"It's my first time in the big town." I smiled. "If you would be so kind as to just tell me where I might find

64

the office, I'd be grateful."

"Right through that door," she replied, gave me a rather pained look, then pointed back over my shoulder.

"I thank you very much," I said, then turned and looked where she had pointed. I stopped cold, dead in my tracks. The door was closed, and I stared at the sign posted on it. There in big, bold, red letters was written:

NO MINORS

I knew immediately that I had been had. I spun around to confront her. But she was gone, no doubt leaning against some wall and killing herself laughing.

During my tenure as an enforcement officer, I had been taught there was no way on the face of the earth that an officer ever went into a barroom when he was working, unless he was responding to a complaint. And since my days in the RCMP, I knew that a barroom in a district where you were stationed was even worse. It was a definite no-no, and that meant no barrooms, either in or out of uniform, working or not. Man, just the thought brought back memories of the Corporal. His voice still boomed in my ears.

"Adams, you horrible little man, if I ever catch you stepping into a barroom in your district, I'll skin you alive."

And now I was supposed to believe a maid, that the Fish and Wildlife Office in Milo was in the bar? I don't think so, I chuckled to myself. After all, this cowboy wasn't born yesterday. I rang the bell again and waited.

"You're kidding me, right?" I asked when the mop lady appeared once more at the top of the steps. I fully expected that she would be enjoying a good laugh at my expense, but one look and I knew she wasn't laughing. In fact, she wasn't even smiling. Again she pointed a finger at the door behind me. She wasn't kidding; she was dead serious about this.

I had this horrible feeling that I was being set up. I just knew that when I walked through that door I would be the laughingstock of the fishery. Fishermen and farmers would laugh for years about the way they got the young Fish Cop to walk into the bar in Milo, thinking it was The Office. Suddenly, I felt sick to my stomach.

I walked over and, turning the doorknob like glass that would break at any second, I slowly opened the door, just a wee crack, and peeked in. I felt that every eye in the place would be on that door, waiting for me to blunder in. Through the wee crack, it appeared that the room was full. Tables were covered with glasses of beer. Everybody was talking and laughing and having a great time. Nobody was paying the least bit of attention to the Fish Cop peeking through the door like a shy little kid. All the while, the Corp's voice was pounding in my head.

"You're here to work, Adams. Don't you even think of setting foot in that barroom in uniform."

I looked around the bar and finally spotted the Senior Officer. He was seated on the last bar chair at the last bar table at the back of the room with his back to the wall.

Entering that room went against the very grain of everything I had ever been taught in law enforcement, but I opened the door wider and prepared to take that first step. I was not at all happy. The Corp wasn't too happy either.

"Adams, you poor excuse for a human being, take one more step and you will be shovelling horseshit for the rest of your career." His roaring words danced in my head.

Reluctantly, I entered the bar and tentatively picked my way among the patrons and their tables. To my amazement, no one paid any attention to me. Oh, sure, one or two looked up and nodded as I walked by, but that was all. To the patrons, it was business as usual, just another day at the office.

"Hey, what's going on here?" I asked when I arrived at the back table. The Senior Officer's makeshift desk was covered with paper, maps, and commercial fishing licences. Sitting out in front of him was a table half-covered with about two dozen glasses of beer, although it didn't look to me as if a single sip had been taken out of any of them. A Fish and Wildlife office in a bar didn't make sense to me; an officer just did not conduct day-to-day business in a barroom.

"Wh-What are you doing in here, in a barroom?" I asked nervously.

"Bobby, you finally made it!" the Senior Officer greeted me, ignoring my questions. "Welcome to the Milo Fish and Wildlife Office. I've been expecting you all day. Where you been?"

"I-I just got here," I stammered as I looked around the barroom.

"Well, don't just stand there gawking around, find

yourself a desk and a chair, and take a load off your feet!" he said giving me a direct order.

"Desk?" I asked. "I don't see any desks in here."

"Yeah, a table. Find yourself a table and chair and bring them over here. You can set up beside me."

"The place is full," I said, scanning the barroom. "I don't even see an empty chair, let alone an empty table."

"We need some office furniture for my partner," the Senior Officer called to the bartender.

"One desk and one chair, comin' up!" he replied. And sure enough, within a couple of minutes he approached, carrying a round table and chair. "There you go, this'll get you started."

"Thanks," I muttered when he plunked the table and chair next to the Senior Officer.

"I'll get you another chair," he added.

"That's okay, I only need one chair," I said. I stood there, nervously looking around the barroom. I knew that at any minute one of the Powers That Be was going to bust in through the door, and my career as a Fish Cop would be over.

"Sit down, Bobby," said the Senior Officer chuckling. "In the Milo Office everybody gets treated equally, everybody gets their own desk and a chair. Are you thirsty, Bobby, would you like a beer?"

"No!" I blurted out, and half the people in the barroom stopped talking and turned to look at me. "I mean no…, no thanks. I-I'm not thirsty," I added meekly. I noted that he didn't have any beer on his table.

"Relax, Bobby, relax. You're too tight," said the Senior Officer, laughing, and all the beer drinkers who had turned to look at me laughed with him. They were still laughing when they went back to talking and drinking their beer.

"Sit, man, sit, before someone gets the idea that you shouldn't be in here."

With that comment, I quickly plunked my butt in the chair. I sat there feeling isolated and alone—and scared. I knew that as soon as the Powers That Be found out about me being in a bar, I was dead meat—history. I'd be out of Fish and Wildlife faster than when I had left the RCMP after they found out I had got engaged. I nervously looked around the barroom, but now no one was paying any attention to me.

"Okay, Bobby, you're in business. There's a lot of work to do before the nets go in the water," the Senior Officer told me. "Here's a book of fishing licences—you can start selling. I'm gonna take a break." And he left the barroom.

I sat there, looking around the room. Looking at the patrons. Looking at the book of fishing licences. What was I supposed to do in here? I asked myself.

"Get out, you fool!" yelled the Corp, who by now was firmly lodged in my head. *"I told you not to enter a barroom. Get out while you still can, before you embarrass the uniform any further."*

It was sound advice, I thought to myself, and I planted my feet. I was ready to hightail it out of there, when I noticed a man get up and stagger towards the bathroom. As soon as he left his seat, the bartender swooped in like a falcon and scooped up his chair. He brought it over to my table and set it down in front of me.

That was the signal the fishermen had been waiting for. The chair had barely touched the floor when the first fisherman arrived.

"You sellin' fishin' licences, laddie?" asked the elderly man who had walked up to my table.

"I-I guess so," I stammered nervously. "Are you a fisherman?"

"Aye, laddie, that I am," he replied, then turned and yelled, rolling his Rs, "Bartender, bring us a round over here!"

"No!" I blurted out for the second time. Again a number of the patrons stopped talking and turned to look at me. "None for me, I don't drink!" I added hastily. This time, no one laughed.

However, the fisherman ignored me as he grabbed the chair and sat down in front of my table. The bartender ignored me, too. He brought the round that was ordered. He placed one beer on my desk, in front of the fisherman, and set the other over on the table that was half-covered with full glasses of beer.

"Now laddie, we're ready to do some business," said the old fisherman. "But first, a drink." I watched as he picked up the glass from my desk and took a long swig of his beer. Then he smacked his lips.

"Don't even think about it, Adams," the Corp's voice boomed in the back of my head. *"Drinking on the job has been the ruination of many a good man."*

"This is your first time on the lake, laddie," he said.

70

"Oh no. No. Well, yes, it's my first time on this lake," I said, "but I've been on many lakes before," I quickly added.

"Aye, laddie, I could tell," he said, mournfully shaking his head. "You're green as grass, laddie. Well, never mind, you look like a bright lad. I guess you'll learn. Now then, I need a licence."

The old guy sat there and sipped his beer and chatted while I issued him his licence. As long as he was seated, not another soul approached the table, but the minute he got up and vacated the chair, another fisherman moved in. Before the second person sat down he, too, turned and raised his arm, pointed two fingers in the air, and called to the bartender.

"A round, my good man, one for me and one for the Fish Cop."

"No! Not for me," I protested quickly, but again my refusal was for naught. The man sat down and the bartender brought another round. The fisherman got his beer, and the beer for the Fish Cop was placed over on the other table.

While I was issuing the second licence, the outside door to the bar suddenly flew open and an ominous figure loomed in the doorway. My first thought was that it was the Powers That Be.

"This is it, Adams!" screamed the Corp. *"You're busted!"*

My head snapped up so fast, I just about got whiplash. My heart was pounding in my chest as my eyes darted around the room looking for a safe place to dive behind. It would be hard to explain the relief I felt

71

when the door slammed shut and I was able to identify the man as another patron.

And so it went for the rest of the afternoon. In an orderly procession, one at a time, the fishermen would come to the Milo Office. So that all could hear, in a loud voice each would order a round of beer before buying his licence. But I could not control the nervous twitch I had every time the door opened and another person entered the bar. All the while, my thirst was building.

I stewed and fretted while we sold licences until six o'clock.

I could have kissed the bartender when he called out, "Drink up, gentlemen! The bar is now closed until seven."

I breathed a sigh of relief and said a prayer that I had dodged a bullet on this. I even thanked those far wiser than I who had seen fit to make it mandatory for all bars in Alberta to close down one hour for supper. It was a good thing, too. I was a nervous wreck as I watched the patrons prepare to leave. They laughed and joked, stood and pulled their coats on, and quaffed the last of their beer before heading out the door. None of them paid any attention to the scared Fish Cop cowering in the Milo Office.

Now, I don't mind admitting that my throat was dry. It was parched and I was dying for something — anything — tall, cold, and wet. I tried not to be too obvious, but the table with the beer for the Fish Cops sure looked inviting. It was packed full; I was sure that it would not hold another glass. You know, I thought to myself as I smacked my lips, I'll bet that no one would miss one glass off that table.

"Have you completely lost your mind, Adams?" the Corp roared again.

"Let's go get some supper, Bobby," called the Senior Officer. His comment almost put me through the roof. I gulped for breath when I turned and looked at him. Sometime during the afternoon he had returned, and I hadn't even noticed him. Man, I thought, he could just as easily have been one of the Powers That Be and I wouldn't have known it. I realized I was shaking like a leaf.

"Go!" I stammered. "Go. But . . . but I can't, what about . . .," and I pointed to the mess that was the Milo Office.

"Leave it," he replied.

"L-leave it?" I couldn't believe what I had just heard.

"Yes, leave it. It'll be all right where it is till we get back."

"Get back! What . . . what do you mean till we get back? You . . . you mean I have to come back in here? We aren't done?"

"Not yet, Bobby," he stated. "Working in the Milo Office isn't a nine-to-five job. This isn't just any ordinary office, you know."

"I've noticed," I said.

"Have you checked in yet?" asked the Senior Officer.

"Checked in? No," I replied, somewhat surprised at the question. "I thought I was just here to help for the day. I didn't know I was staying."

"You're here for the duration, Bobby," he said and

73

laughed. "We got a lot of work to do yet. You better go and check in here for tonight. We'll go across the street to the Chinaman's Café for supper. It's the only place in town to eat. I'll meet you there."

He got up and walked out the front door. I stood there with my mouth open. If I had found the location of the Milo Office hard to believe, what I had just witnessed was — witnessed, hell, what I'd been a party to — it was incredible. I looked at his desk and mine. Everything was there; papers, licences, maps, records, everything was scattered across the bar table, exactly where it was when the last licence was sold.

"Adams, have you completely lost your mind? You can't leave government documents lying around in this bar unsupervised!" the Corp's voice thundered.

I just stood there, unable to move.

"The bar's closed, young fella," the bartender stated firmly.

"So, it appears, is the Milo Fish and Wildlife Office," I muttered.

Everything about this day flew right in the face of everything I had ever been taught. During all my training when I was a Horse Cop, I had been cautioned — no, it had been drilled into me — not to be in a bar in uniform. And now, here I was, up to my neck in beer. I took one last look at the table full of beer, and the fruits of our labour that we were about to leave unattended in the Milo Office, then I turned and walked towards the door.

Man, I thought, if the Corp could see this, he would roll over in his grave.

THE SHEEP KILLER

"Harry, they tell me you got the best deal in town on a good rifle," I said to the old grey-haired gentleman behind the counter.

"Who told you that pack of lies, Bobby?" Harry asked.

"A little bird," I replied.

"Don't believe the little bird," Harry advised me. "Little birds don't always know what they're talking about."

"The little bird said, Bobby, if you need a good rifle you go talk to your friend Harry. He gives people a fifty-percent discount."

"Fifty percent?" Harry wailed. "Fifty percent! Why, Bobby, that's highway robbery, I never gave fifty percent to anybody in my life."

"That's what the little bird said, Harry," I assured

him. "The little bird also said you'd deny it."

"What are you going to shoot, Bobby? Do you just want a varmint gun, or are you gonna shoot big-game animals as well?" he asked.

"Well, Harry, the first thing I'm gonna do is shoot a sheep killer. I've got this Hutterite, Big Jake, he's at my door every day complaining about this bloody coyote that's killing his sheep. I offered him one of the shells I'd been issued, so that he could shoot it, but he told me he didn't have a rifle. I don't think he believed me when I told him I didn't have a rifle either. I can only afford one rifle, Harry. It has to be something I can load up or down to shoot everything from a fox to a bear."

"Antelope, Bobby, are you just going to shoot an antelope, then?" he asked.

"Antelope, deer, elk, moose, bear. You name it, Harry. If there's a season on it, if it gets hit by a car, or it causes damage, I may have to shoot it," I replied.

"What about the government rifle, Bobby? Why don't you use the rifle they give you?" Harry asked.

"Like I said, Harry, they didn't issue me a rifle," I replied.

"Didn't you phone them?" he asked. "You should phone them and tell them you need a rifle to kill the coyote."

"Oh, I did, Harry. I did," I assured him. "I called the Powers That Be and told them I needed a rifle to kill the Hutterite's coyote."

"And what did they say?"

"They told me to use the bullets they issued me with," I replied.

76

"What do you mean, Bobby?" he asked.

"Well, you see, Harry, they do give me shells. One box, twenty shells a year. In fact, as soon as you sell me one of those good rifles you got for fifty percent off, I've got two boxes of .303 shells to trade."

Harry shook his head; he couldn't believe what he had just heard. Then he turned to the gun rack that ran the length of the wall. He walked over and picked a rifle off the rack and returned.

"Here's your rifle, Bobby," he said. He flipped the bolt open and he looked into the breach before handing me the rifle.

I took the rifle and looked it over carefully. This was going to be the first large-calibre rifle I had ever bought, and I was going to make sure it was the right one.

"A brand-new Parker-Hale .30-06. Now that's what I call a rifle, Harry," I said, chuckling.

I ran my hand along the shiny, steel-blue barrel. I felt the smoothness of the varnished stock. This was the day I had dreamed of since I was a kid on the Stump Farm—getting my own rifle. I lifted the rifle to my shoulder. It fit perfectly. This was my rifle, all right. It was made for me.

"That's right," Harry said. "It's the best all-purpose rifle money can buy. You can load it up with a heavy-grain bullet for moose or bear, or you can load it down with a light-grain bullet to shoot that coyote that's bothering the Hutterites. This is your rifle, Bobby," he assured me.

Then I looked at the price tag: $74.99.

"Bring me a different one, Harry. I just want something I can shoot a sheep-killing coyote with. This is a nice rifle, but I can't afford that much. If I brought this rifle home, Mar would shoot me on the spot. I think maybe I better have a look at an army surplus .303 British to go with the two boxes of shells the Division has given me."

"No. No. Bobby, don't get excited!" Harry laughed. "You don't want an old .303. You want a good rifle. One that you can depend on. And I haven't even given you your discount yet." Harry paused, then winked at me. "You did say you wanted a discount, didn't you?"

"Harry," I said, "at this price I'm gonna need more than a discount. And even then, even if you give me fifty percent, I don't know how I'm going to explain it to Mar."

"Tell your good wife that Harry gave you a good deal," he said and chuckled. "You know, Bobby, women always like it when you get a good deal."

"Oh yeah. Sure," I mumbled. "I'd like to see you try to justify to Mar that you spent next month's rent on a rifle. You could even stress that you spent her money to do government work—shooting a coyote on a Hutterite colony. You can be sure she'll love that."

Harry just laughed as he took out a piece of paper and started scribbling numbers.

"Let's see," he mumbled to himself. "Seventy-five dollars less twenty-five percent. That's—"

"That's not enough," I interjected, before he finished his calculations.

Harry ignored me and finished figuring. Harry

stopped long enough to look up and give me another big wink. "Then I'll take off another fifteen percent," Harry mumbled again. "Now that would be—"

"Still not enough," I informed him once more.

"Hold on, Bobby, I'm not finished yet," he chuckled. "And then, I'll take off another five . . ." He paused again and looked up at me. "No, Bobby, that would only be forty-five percent off, wouldn't it?" he said seriously. "I'll tell you what I'm gonna do, let's take off another ten percent. How does that sound?"

Harry's pen continued to scratch numbers and when he finished, there was a long string of numbers, down the length of the page.

"That's fifty percent, Harry," I said. "Why didn't you just take fifty percent off the top in the first place. You could have saved all that figuring!"

"Don't be so sure, Bobby," Harry said, chuckling. "Believe only half of what you see, and nothing of what you hear. Everything is not always what it seems. Anyway, as I said before, I never give anyone fifty percent. Now, do we have a deal?"

Harry had me where he wanted me, and I wanted that gun. I had not let go of it. I admired it. I pointed it at a coyote pelt that I spotted hanging on the wall at the end of the building. Harry knew I was hooked. I was going to buy the rifle. But I had absolutely no idea how I was going to break the news to Mar.

"Okay, we have a deal," I replied and smiled at Harry.

"You made a good decision, Bobby," Harry said. He chuckled happily and gave me another big wink. "Now let me get you a scope—"

"Hold it, Harry," I replied in a hurry. "I'm pushing my luck with the rifle. I don't need a scope." In my weakened condition, I didn't even want to see the scope.

"But a good rifle like that should have a scope, Bobby. You need a scope for shooting coyotes," Harry said wisely. "You have to make some long shots out on the prairie."

"A hundred yards, Harry. A hundred yards, that's all. Big Jake, the sheep boss out at the Colony, told me that you can approach to within a hundred yards of the coyote that's killing his sheep. Big Jake says he sees the coyote almost every day, usually when it's killing one of his sheep. It sounds like the coyote's become accustomed to seeing Big Jake around and is easy to approach. I don't think I'll need a scope to shoot a hundred yards."

"You should have a scope," Harry persisted.

"I don't need a scope, Harry. Anyway, I can't afford this rifle, let alone a scope. But I do need to trade you some .303 shells for some .30-06."

"I can do that for you," Harry said. "But you should really consider the scope."

"Hold the scope, Harry," I said. "Maybe another time."

The brand-new rifle and I arrived home well before Mar finished work at the bank. I laid it on the table and stewed about breaking the news to Mar. Then I had an idea.

We lived only a couple of blocks from the bank, but

I drove over and picked her up. I even opened the door for her and let her enter the house first. I was right behind her when she entered the kitchen.

"What's this?" she asked and stopped short as she looked at the brand-new rifle lying on the kitchen table. She walked over and picked up the card laying beside the rifle and opened it and read out loud:

HAPPY BIRTHDAY, BOB

LOVE, MAR

"Thank you, pet," I warbled happily. "How did you know this was the exact rifle I wanted?"

Mar was not impressed.

Bright and early the next morning, I turned the Forestry Green station wagon north and headed out of town. On the seat beside me was my brand-new .30-06 rifle. I was off to shoot me a sheep killer, but first I had to see how straight it shot. I stopped at a farmer's field where a small hill provided a good backstop. I set two soup cans on a couple of fence posts, then paced off a hundred yards. I turned and faced the posts. I sat down and loaded five rounds into the magazine.

I put the sights on the first soup can, took a breath, exhaled slowly, then squeezed the trigger. The rifle roared, and the soup can jumped into the air before spinning to the ground. The second can performed exactly the same way.

"Two shots. Two soup cans. By gosh, Harry was right, this is a good rifle," I said chuckling. "C'mon, Big Jake, bring on your sheep killer!"

Big Jake was waiting for me when I arrived at the Colony. When I drove into the yard, he barrelled out of the outhouse and charged over to the station wagon. Big Jake didn't seem that anxious to get out in the field and kill the coyote. First, we had to stop and have a coffee with a few of the other bosses. Big Jake made sure that everyone within shouting distance knew that after today his sheep would once again be safe out in the top pasture. Today, Big Jake was *the* man on the Colony, and he wanted to make sure that everybody knew it.

When a sufficient quantity of coffee had been guzzled, Big Jake and I left the gathering, but the gathering did not leave us. Every single boss followed us to the station wagon. Every single boss decided that it was he who should accompany me out to the top pasture. All wanted to see the sheep killer die. And they all wanted to ride in the Forestry Green station wagon.

"Big Jake, tell them no," I said before I unlocked the doors. "You tell them I'll only take one person in the vehicle with me. And that person better be able to show me where the sheep killer is."

Big Jake had absolutely no trouble telling everyone that it was his sheep that were being killed. That he was the sheep boss and it was he who knew where the sheep killer hung out. Therefore, it was he, Big Jake, who would accompany me to the field.

"Is this the gun you're going to use?" Big Jake asked when he climbed into the passenger seat.

"That's it," I replied. "That's a pretty nice-looking rifle, wouldn't you say?"

"Where's the scope?" Big Jake asked. He didn't seem to be very impressed with the rifle. He turned to check out the back seat. Big Jake figured there had to be another rifle, one with a scope on it.

"I don't need a scope," I informed him.

"I never saw a rifle without a scope," he said. Big Jake leaned over to get a real good look at a rifle that didn't have a scope on it.

"Do you have a rifle?" I asked.

"No. The Colony doesn't allow guns," he replied, still giving my new rifle the once-over.

"So, how many rifles have you seen, then?"

"Lots," he said lots. "You'll never shoot that coyote without a scope."

"Well, I'm a pretty good shot, you know."

"You'll need a scope to shoot this coyote," Big Jake assured me.

"I thought you said we could get within a hundred yards of him," I said, reminding him of our previous conversations.

"We can," he replied, "but you won't hit him without a scope."

Big Jake had directed us through a series of gates above the creek bank and out across the prairie. I was inching the green station wagon over the rough, frozen ground when Big Jake suddenly yelled.

"There he is! There's the sheep killer!"

I slammed on the brakes and looked where Big Jake was pointing. Off to our right, across the field, on the far side of a slough, at the edge of the tall grass was an animal. It was lying flat, crouching on its stomach facing us.

"There he is," Big Jake yelled again. "Quick, shoot him before he runs away."

The animal lay very still, watching us, from a distance of well over three hundred yards.

"I think I'll drive up a little closer," I said to Big Jake. I was thinking that three-hundred-plus yards was a little far for open sights, and if Big Jake was right, I had a couple of hundred yards to play with before the coyote spooked.

"No," yelled Big Jake excitedly. "If you try to get any closer, he'll turn and run into the bush."

"How do you know that?" I asked.

"Some other guys have tried to shoot him, but they all missed."

"Tell me, Jake, how far is that coyote away from us?" I asked.

Jake looked out across the prairie, carefully measuring the distance.

"A hundred yards," he finally said.

"That's what I thought. If that's a hundred yards, Jake, I'm two feet tall."

"Oh no," Jake said seriously, "you're taller than that."

"You know, Jake, the more I look at that coyote, the more I think it's not a coyote," I said.

"That's a coyote, all right," Big Jake assured me. "That's the coyote that's been killing my sheep."

"I'm just going to have a look at him through my binoculars," I said. I really wanted to get a better look at the sheep killer before taking a shot at it. I reached under the front seat and pulled out the beat-up old binocular case.

Through the wonky binoculars, I looked at the sheep

killer with both eyes open. I closed my right eye and tried to get a look with the left. I turned and twisted the lens every which way as I tried to get a good look at the coyote through those wonky binoculars. But even a move from Brooks to Strathmore had not improved the binoculars I had been issued the day I was sworn in. From three hundred yards away, all I could make out was a fuzzy light-brown ball in a field of fuzzier grass and even fuzzier willows.

"I don't know, Jake, I still don't think that's a coyote."

"Let me look," said Big Jake as he reached for the binoculars.

"What do you think, Jake?" I asked. But Jake wasn't listening, he was concentrating on my binoculars. He seemed to be pointing them in every direction except where the sheep killer lay crouched in the grass.

"Does that look like a sheep-killin' coyote to you?" I asked again.

"I don't think these things are very good," he replied. He lowered the binoculars and looked them over carefully. Then he shook them vigorously.

"Do binoculars work better if you give them a good shake like that?" I asked.

Big Jake stopped shaking the binoculars and returned them to his eyes.

"I can't see very well through these things," he stated. "Maybe there's something wrong with them. I think you should have got a new pair of binoculars when you got the rifle."

"You just have to learn how to focus them

properly," I assured him. "I don't think I'm going to shoot until I can confirm that it's a coyote. What do you think?"

"That's a coyote," Big Jake confirmed his previous identification of the sheep killer. "I can see him real good now." At that moment he had the binoculars pointed skyward. "That's the coyote that's been killing my sheep," Big Jake insisted. "I've seen him many times. He's a coyote all right. You better shoot him."

I was convinced, as was Big Jake, that it was a sheep killer. I got out of the station wagon and pussyfooted to the rear. I dropped one round in the chamber and closed the bolt on my brand-new rifle. I had no trouble hitting the soup cans at a hundred yards, but a coyote at three-hundred-plus yards — now, that was a different story.

The front sight completely hid the coyote. Right now, I was kicking myself for not taking Harry's advice. Even the cheapest scope in the gun shop would have been far better than what I had.

"Shoot him," I heard Big Jake urge me once again. "That's the coyote that's been killing my sheep."

Once more I took aim at the sheep killer. "Here goes a Hail Mary," I muttered as I slowly squeezed the trigger. The rifle barked. The sheep killer did a little flop, then lay still.

"You got him!" howled a very excited Big Jake. "You got him!" Big Jake jumped out of the station wagon and raced over to where I was down on one knee. He slapped me on the back so hard, I thought he was going to drive his hand right through me.

I stood up and then just like they always did in the good old Western movies, I looked Big Jake in the eye, smiled, and blew the smoke from the end of the barrel. I pulled the bolt back and watched the ejected empty cartridge flip harmlessly through the air and land in the prairie wool. I returned the rifle to the front seat of the green station wagon. Hitting a coyote with open sights was no problem for this coyote killer.

"I want that pelt," Big Jake demanded. Big Jake was serious and asserting his authority. After all, it was his land. It was his sheep the sheep killer had been feasting on. Yes, Big Jake was staking his claim, and rightly so.

"What are you gonna do with the pelt?" I asked.

"I can get five bucks for a good coyote pelt."

"Well, I don't know about that, Jake," I said, sprinkling a little water on his parade. "Maybe we should talk about that for a minute."

"No. No talking. I want that pelt," Big Jake said adamantly.

"You know, Jake, I had to buy this rifle, and I had to come all the way out here. And after all, I was the one who shot it."

"No! That's my pelt," protested Big Jake.

"Well, you know, Jake," I said, "the Fish and Wildlife Division might have a claim on that pelt, too. After all, they provided the shell, the vehicle, and the gas to get us out here. The more I think about it, the more I think we might have to split that coyote three ways. Let's see now, the way I figure it, that would be about $1.66 each. Whaddaya think, Jake, is that how you see it?"

"I'm going to give you some sheep meat," Big Jake suddenly blurted out as we began our walk over to where the sheep killer lay.

"Sheep meat! Whoa up a second, Jake, I don't think so. I don't even like lamb, let alone a stinkin' ol' sheep," I said.

"I'll give you a sack of potatoes, too," he said, quickly upping the ante. Then his face lit up and he added, "Everybody likes potatoes."

I laughed. "No. No, Jake. Slow down. I was only kidding. I don't want any potatoes. I don't need any potatoes. I don't need anything."

"I can throw in some chickens. Do you need some chickens?" asked Big Jake.

By the time Big Jake got around to offering the chickens, we had arrived at the sheep killer. We both looked at the animal lying in the grass.

Big Jake was speechless as we stood over the sheep killer. He just stood there staring, with his mouth open. He couldn't say a word. His jaw started to tremble.

"You . . . you shot him, he's dead," Big Jake stammered. He finally found his voice, but it was barely more than a whisper.

"Yeah, I know," I replied. "You know, Jake, I think you and Harry were both right, I should get a scope for the rifle. I'll try to get rid of that old set of binoculars, too."

"You . . . you . . .," Big Jake's voice was getting stronger now.

"You know, Jake, I was thinkin' $1.66 docsn't really go that far. If you can get five bucks for the pelt, you should take it. In fact, you can have my share and the Government's too."

And then, Big Jake's voice returned in force.

"You . . . you shot my sheepdog," Big Jake roared, and his voice reverberated across the prairie.

THE LONG-NECKED GOOSE

It was a typical fall day on the Alberta prairie. The sun was shining and there was not a single cloud in the bluest of blue skies. There was a crispness in the air, a tinge of frost, just a hint of things to come.

Earlier in the week, I had made arrangements to meet with a Horse Cop from Drumheller to go over a court case. It would have been a shame to waste such a beautiful day sitting inside, so we opted to do our business outdoors. Parked high on a bank overlooking one of the Ducks Unlimited projects near Irricana, we had a great view. The lake on this quiet day was calm, flat, like a mirror. It was a great day to be out.

"Listen," I said, and held up a hand for silence. We had spread out our lunches on the hood of my Forestry

Green station wagon. We were both leaning against the front fender, gazing out across the lake, eating our lunch, when a series of calls drifted across the water.

"There, did you hear that?" I asked as the sounds waned and died away in the distance.

"I did," replied the constable. "What was it, geese?"

"Swans," I replied very knowledgeably. I dug under the front seat on the driver's side and pulled out my wonky binoculars. Getting the best focus that I could, I scanned the far shore.

"Can you see them?" he asked.

"No. They must be in one of the little bays on the far side of the lake."

"Lemme look, I'd like to see them too," he said. He grabbed my binoculars and pointed them in the direction of the sounds.

"You might want to use your own binoculars," I mentioned to him as he tried desperately to focus mine.

"I don't have any," he said.

"You're lucky," I grumbled. "In a manner of speaking, neither do I."

"Nope, I can't see them either. These binoculars are a piece of junk," he snorted disgustedly as he tossed my binoculars onto the front seat.

We ate a leisurely lunch and then hauled out the file. Occasionally, our review would be interrupted by the call of a swan, and we would both glance towards the far side of the lake. But the swans never showed themselves.

A slight breeze had blown up and sent a ripple across what had been the mirrored lake. We decided to have a last coffee and enjoy the day before we headed in our separate directions.

"Do you get many hunters on this lake?" asked the Mountie.

"Oh yeah, a few from time to time," I replied, "but it really depends on the weather. A lot of ducks fly across the narrows." I pointed to the bay out in front of us. "See that heavy patch of bulrushes out in the water?" I asked. The bulrushes were only a couple of hundred yards from us across the water.

"Yeah," he said.

"Hunters can reach the reeds by wading in from the far side; the water's fairly shallow over there. Then they hide themselves and bang away at any duck that flies by. But today is just too nice a day to hunt ducks," I stated.

"I don't know how anyone can hide in there," he scoffed. "Those puny reeds don't look like they could hide a duck, let alone a man."

"Oh, they work pretty good," I assured him. "In fact, you'd have a tough time seeing someone in there."

"Oh, I'll bet. Anyway, I guess I better hit the road, before someone misses me," he chuckled.

"Yeah, I better see if I can find me some hunters to check, too," I replied.

"See you in court!" He laughed.

Just then, there was a heck of a racket on the far side of the lake. Loud squawking. Wings were flapping and slapping water. We both stopped and looked, scanning the far shore.

"The swans are up," I informed my friend the Horse

Cop. Sure enough, several large white birds appeared.

"Yeah, I know, I can see them," he said, his voice almost a whisper.

"You're in luck," I said. "You're gonna get a real good look at 'em. If I'm not mistaken, they're coming right at us."

"You think so?" he asked.

"Yeah, I think so. With any luck at all, they might go right over us."

"Well, I guess I'm not that worried if someone misses me," he said with a chuckle. "I think I'll just sit here and watch for a minute."

"Me too," I replied. "I never get tired of watching swans fly. They're a magnificent bird and so graceful."

There we stood, on the banks of a prairie lake, the Horse Cop and the Fish Cop, watching a flock of swans winging toward us.

"Man, are they ever big!" said the Horse Cop as the birds flew closer. "You know, I've never really paid any attention to them before, they're humongous."

"They're big, all right," I agreed. "You know, if we were at Namaka Lake right now, I'd be shouting at the top of my lungs . . ." I paused for a second. Why not, I thought, there's no one but me and the Horse Cop for miles around. So I opened my mouth and as loud as I could, I called to the lake, I called to the prairie, I called to the crisp breeze, and I called to the imaginary hunter.

"*Swans!*" I bellowed loud and clear. "*S   Don't shoot! They're swans!*" The Horse Cop step   back and he looked at me as if I had lost my mind.

"Man, now that felt good," I chortled.

"What do you think you're doing?" he asked. "It sounds to me like you've just lost your marbles."

"Showing you one of my crime-prevention techniques," I grinned. "And do you know what would happen then?"

"I have no idea," he assured me.

"Invariably some idiot would jump out of the bulrushes and shoot the first swan that flew by," I told him.

"Sure, sure, and if I believe that one, you've got a bridge to sell me, right?" he snickered.

"No, honestly, I'm not kidding," I replied. "You may find it hard to believe, but I've seen some hunters who are actually mesmerized when they see birds flying. I've walked right up to hunters, and they didn't know I was there. I know it sounds crazy, but some hunters didn't realize they had company even when I spoke to them."

"You're really serious, aren't you?" he asked.

"Scout's honour," I replied.

He just shook his head. We both turned our attention back to the swans.

As the birds neared the shoreline and our vehicles, they veered to the right, taking them out of harm's way, away from our vehicles. Now the flock was going to pass over the bulrushes. Although they were a couple of hundred yards from where we stood, they were still close enough that we could hear their pinions squeaking as the birds winged past.

The lead bird had just flown over the reeds when the tranquility of the peaceful prairie day was shattered. Without any warning a figure suddenly sprang up, like a jack-in-the-box, from the middle of the bulrushes. And he was pointing a gun at the swans.

"Don't shoot, you idiot!" I screamed as loud as I could. *"Don't shoot — they're swans!"*

But I had seen this scenario before. The guy was in a world of his own, concentrating on the birds. He was oblivious to us.

"Hit the dirt!" I yelled when I realized that the hunter, the swans, the vehicles, and the cops were all in line. The first shot rang out as we both dove behind my Forestry Green station wagon. Two more shots echoed in rapid succession.

I don't know about my buddy the Horse Cop, but I for one was scared. I was shaking, and my knees were knocking like crazy. I scrunched down lower when the first pellets rained down on the Horse Cop, on the Fish Cop, and on my Forestry Green station wagon.

I looked at the Horse Cop, he was on his belly halfway under my Forestry Green station wagon, and he had his hands cupped over his head for added protection. Yeah, I thought, he's scared too. If there had been a gopher hole there, I'm sure he would have gone down it; however, he would have had to beat me to it. We cowered behind the vehicle for several minutes.

"I think it's safe to take a look now," I whispered to him when the pellets stopped falling and there were no more shots. Slowly he looked up.

"Where did he come from?" asked the Horse Cop and his eyes were bugged right out as he relived the adventure.

"From the bulrushes," I replied. "You know, the

ones that wouldn't hide a duck."

"I didn't think there was anybody else around for miles," he mumbled.

"Me neither. Did you see a car when you drove in?" I asked. "I know I didn't."

"No, I didn't," he replied. "But that idiot tried to kill us."

"I think you should go and arrest him," I said and watched as his eyes got even wider.

"Me?" he snorted. "But . . . but he's got a gun!"

"So what? You got one, too," I said.

"Why don't you go?" he asked.

"I would, but I can't," I replied. "I don't have a gun. Remember they don't give Fish Cops guns."

"I'll give you mine," he replied seriously.

"I'm not qualified to shoot your gun," I informed him.

"Well, it's a wildlife case," he argued. "That makes it your responsibility, not mine."

"Wrong again," I said and smiled. "Swans are migratory birds, that's federal legislation. That makes them your responsibility."

About that time, the sounds of splashing and thrashing through the bulrushes could be heard above our discussion. Slowly, we both rose to our knees and very carefully peeked over the hood of the vehicle.

Neither of us spoke as we watched the hunter slosh his way through the water and thick growth. When he got to the edge of the bulrushes, he stood there looking at the bird floating about halfway between him and dry land.

"Nice shot, nimrod!" I yelled. He stopped in his tracks and stared at us. We both hunkered lower, expecting another shot. "Now that you got him, what're you gonna do?"

"That's my goose. I'll get it," he called back and started back towards his hiding place.

"Goose?" asked the Horse Cop with a somewhat bewildered look on his face. "I thought you said they were swans."

"Oh, it's a swan all right," I said.

My partner and I stood up and watched as the hunter pulled off his waders.

"I'd think twice before I did that," I yelled. "That water's going to be awfully cold. I wouldn't be wading in there without my boots on if I was you."

"It's okay, I was out there earlier this morning," he said. "The water's too deep to wade. I'll just swim out and get it," he added. I couldn't believe it when he took off his coat. Then he peeled off his shirt and pulled down his trousers. Dressed only in his drawers, he started back through the bulrushes.

"Don't do that!" I yelled at him. "I'll come over and get you and we can wait till it drifts in to shore."

"No way!" he replied. "That's the first goose I've seen all day, and I'm not going to lose it." He burst through the bulrushes and without a second's hesitation strode into the water. In two steps he was up to his waist, one more step and he was swimming towards his kill.

"Now, I know this guy is yours," I said to the Horse Cop. "He's got to be nuts, swimming in that water. This is a mental case if I ever saw one. Mental cases are definitely your responsibility."

The Horse Cop ignored my logic.

The hunter did exactly as he said he would: he swam out and retrieved the bird. He grasped the swan by the head and towed it through the frigid waters, but instead of going back to his blind, he continued swimming straight towards the bank where we were waiting.

With the swans head draped over one shoulder and the neck and body hanging down his back, he waded ashore. Using his free hand, he scratched and clawed his way up a very steep embankment with his burden. He dragged his prey across the prairie, the body and the feet dragging on the ground behind him as he walked towards us. I noticed that he had a huge grin on his face; actually, I believe it was frozen on his face. He was as happy as a lark and as cold as an icicle.

"Tell me, sir, what is it that you think you have there?" I asked.

He tried to respond, but he was shaking all over. His body was covered in goosebumps and his grinning lips were a deep, dark, purply blue. The only sound I heard was that of chattering teeth.

"You better get in the car before you chip all your ivories," I said.

He looked at me suspiciously, and then at the swan.

"Don't worry, we'll make sure nothing happens to the bird," I assured him.

Reluctantly, he dropped the swan and staggered forward a couple of steps. I grabbed him, opened the door, and helped him in, then went around to the driver's side, got in, and started the engine. I turned the heater to high.

"Why'd you shoot a swan?" I asked when he warmed up to the point where he could finally speak.

"Swan?" he replied. "I didn't shoot a swan, I shot a goose. It's a goose. A snow goose."

"If that were a goose, sir, it would be the longest-necked goose in the world," I declared.

"It would?" he asked. Then he turned and looked long and hard at the swan lying on the prairie grass.

"Didn't you hear me yell 'Swans, don't shoot, they're swans'?" I asked.

"Hear you?" he chattered. Then he paused and gave me the strangest look. "How could I hear you when I didn't see you? I didn't even know you were here."

A look of concern crossed his face, his brow furrowed, and for a few seconds he was deep in thought. Then he looked me right in the eye, and asked in all sincerity, "Where'd you guys come from anyway? How'd you get here?"

My friend the Horse Cop just rolled his eyes in disbelief.

PADDY,
THE LYNX-HUNTING FOOL

The Strathmore Fish and Wildlife District was barely a year old in the fall of 1963. The perception that the District was akin to an old folks' home, a place of very little activity, had long since been proven false. The myth had been laid to rest, and with it went the kidding and teasing.

"C'mon, boy, let's go!" George yodelled excitedly as he pulled up in front of my house. I was in the process of mowing the lawn and had not been expecting anyone, let alone George. But that was one of the neat things about George — he had a knack for showing up at the darndest times. And I could count on some sort of adventure being the reason for the visit.

Today was no exception. There was a grin lighting up his face that could be seen for miles. As had been the rule lately, George was not alone. In the place of honour, the front seat, right next to George and crowded in as close as he could get, was Paddy. Paddy's back feet were planted firmly on the seat beside George, and his front feet were up on the dash. Paddy was a beagle that George had conscripted to assist us in tracking down the many lynx that had invaded the prairie, particularly the Strathmore district, in '62 and '63, and Paddy the beagle was a lynx-hunting fool.

Paddy had shared many monumental occasions with me. He had been there for instance, on September 19, 1963, the day my oldest daughter was born. I was celebrating her birth with some of my friends, enjoying a rare day off, when a call came that a lynx was killing chickens a short four miles from town. I was really in no shape to chase a lynx, let alone try to catch it.

"It'll have to wait until tomorrow," I declared. "I'm not going out there now."

"Don't worry, boy," George sang out, for he was one of the boys helping me celebrate. It was obvious that George would far sooner chase a lynx than celebrate. "C'mon, we'll take my car. We'll all go help you. We'll just grab Paddy on the way out of town. With Paddy, it won't take us no time at all to whip down there and pick up that lynx."

Now, George didn't own Paddy. In fact, George didn't even own a dog, but he never let a little thing like that stop him. With George, the elder statesman of the group, driving, we left my house. I didn't let a little thing like chasing a lynx interfere with my celebrating. I was still celebrating when George stopped to pick up Paddy, the hound dog.

"I need Paddy," George told the owner. It was George's way of asking. A request was less likely to be refused if you just told someone rather than asking. "We've got another lynx just south of town." Before the owner could agree or disagree, George had Paddy in the front seat of his car. While George drove the four miles to meet the lynx, I kept celebrating.

"I last saw him down by that patch of trees," the farmer informed George.

"This won't take long," George assured him. "We even brought Paddy with us. Paddy's a lynx-hunting fool; he hasn't missed one yet."

Paddy was a free-roaming dog, but he roamed so slowly that there was no need to leash him. I watched as Paddy carefully left the safety of the front seat. Immediately, his nose went to the ground, he sniffed a couple of times, then lifted his head and pointed his nose toward the sky. I thought for a minute that he was going to let out a bark or, better yet, howl "LYNX", but no such luck; Paddy wasn't that excited. He yawned, and then lay down.

"C'mon, Paddy," George warbled, "let's go catch a lynx." George bounded off through the grass. Paddy, not wanting to be left alone, slowly got up, stretched, and then padded after George. With George and Paddy in the lead, I and my fellow celebrators, the farmer, and his young son, all tramped through the tall grass and the Russian thistle towards the clump of poplars and willows. Paddy was about to prove once more that he belonged with the great cat hunters of the world.

"This is a good place," George said. "We'll be able to

follow Paddy and see how he works."

At the clump of trees, we all followed Paddy as he put his lynx-hunting nose to work. We watched as Paddy snuffled through the grass. We watched as he sniffed the base of a big poplar. We watched as he stopped, lifted his leg, and watered the tree. We watched as he checked first one clump of willows and then another. We watched until there was only Paddy's wagging tail showing as he worked his way in under the deadfall. We watched and we watched. Eventually, we all sat down.

"Woof," called Paddy as he disappeared from sight.

"I think that Paddy's got him!" yelled the farmer's kid, jumping to his feet.

"You'll know when he's got him," George replied. Then he turned to the farmer. "Are you sure this is where you saw the lynx?"

"Yep, right down by these trees," he replied. "This is where he was when I phoned."

"Yep, right by these trees," echoed the youngster.

Paddy had come out from under the deadfall and was now circling the area. He roamed through the trees, back and forth, but found nothing.

"Maybe this isn't going to be as easy as we thought after all, boy," George said and laughed. "We better give him a hand."

Slowly our crew spread out to assist Paddy in the search for the elusive lynx. We left the trees and waded back into the tall grass and the Russian thistle. We shouted and yelled as we zigzagged our way around the area.

Meanwhile, we had all lost sight of Paddy, the lynx-hunting fool. He was off checking on other matters of interest to him. Then suddenly, from somewhere in the tall grass, Paddy howled.

"AAARRRROOOO!" The plaintive wail drifted across the field. It left no doubt in the minds of those of us who had heard it in the past. Paddy had just howled "LYNX!"

"AAARRRROOOO!" he wailed again, The scent was fresh. I felt a tingle right up and down my spine. I could see why houndsmen yearned for the thrill of the hunt and the howl of the hound. It was definitely something special. There was no doubt, Paddy was a revered member of our team.

"He's got him!" yelled George excitedly. "He's got him! I knew it. I knew he would do it. Paddy's never let us down yet."

The celebrators, as well as the farmer and his kid, took off on a dead run. We raced through the grass heading for the sound of the howling hound. But Paddy was not standing around waiting; he was moving back into the trees.

"AAARRRROOOO!" Paddy howled in his finest voice. All six of us raced into the trees.

"Check the trees," yelled George. "He'll be up a tree somewhere." Instantly, like robots, all heads snapped up and all eyes looked skyward. Slowly, we walked through the area searching in the trees for a sign of the cat. But there was no cat in the trees. Meanwhile, Paddy, with his nose to the ground, was still howling "LYNX!"

"The dumb hound dog's just runnin' round in circles," said the kid. There was just a tinge of sarcasm and a whole lot of disappointment in his voice.

"He's not just running around, he's following a scent," I replied. "There's a lynx here and you just keep your eyes on ol' Paddy. He'll find him."

"Hmphf, I'll bet," scoffed the kid.

The trail took Paddy back into the tall grass. Here he picked up a little speed, now that the going was easier, and headed straight for another clump of brush, followed closely by the cat hunters. We charged into the second clump of trees and immediately started to search high in the trees. Paddy, with his nose to the ground, was still howling "LYNX!" But once again there was no lynx. Soon we realized that Paddy had left the trees and was now heading back to the first clump. Once more, we followed.

"That's the dumbest hound dog I ever saw," declared the kid. "I'm not gonna chase after some stupid dog all day."

At that point the kid left us. We also lost a couple of the revellers. They, too, had tired of the sport and flopped down to rest in the tall grass.

We had not lost George. He was close on Paddy's rapidly wagging tail as he entered the first clump of trees for the second time. Paddy continued to howl "LYNX!" to tell us that he still had a hot trail. In a short time, sniffing and baying, he raced back to the second clump of trees.

This time, I did not follow Paddy and George. I stopped to talk to the two who were now lying flat on

105

their backs admiring the sky. They were discussing the merits of returning to town and spending their time doing something constructive, like more celebrating.

"This is a waste of time," one of them said. "The dog's probably just chasing a smart old rabbit." I turned to watch George and the hound moving back to the first stand of trees.

"Come here, George," I called to him. "Take a second and cool off. I want to show you something you ain't gonna believe."

"I don't know what's in there, boy," George panted as he walked up to us, "but whatever it is, it's sure got Paddy's attention."

"Watch the trees on the left," I said.

We both stood there looking, both amazed, as a lynx emerged from the trees. It took a look in the direction of Paddy, who was just leaving the other stand of trees. Then it calmly walked into the tall grass, heading toward the hound. Paddy and the lynx passed within feet of each other. Paddy didn't look twice; he only trusted his nose. That was one darn smart lynx, he could out-think that hound dog. But now we could see him, and we trusted our eyes. Now we had him. We left Paddy to his nose and his hot trail; we were now on the heels of the wily lynx. The cat broke into a lope. Leaving the scattered clumps of brush, the tall grass, and the Russian thistle, it headed for a small canal that was fairly well treed.

"We got him now!" George yelled over his shoulder. "We got him now, boy. He'll tree when he hits the canal." I was right behind him. However, we hadn't counted on how smart that lynx really was. He did not tree when he reached the canal; in fact, he showed little respect for the canal at all. My buddy, George, was right on his tail when the lynx jumped and easily sailed over the canal.

I had to hand it to George, he didn't hesitate for a second. Like a broad-jumper, he followed the lynx. Leaping high into the air, he stretched one leg out and reached for the far bank. A second later, there was a tremendous eruption, like a depth charge, in front of me. My buddy George landed right smack dab in the middle of the canal. The lynx calmly looked over its shoulder, then disappeared over the far bank.

I was not far behind George, and I laughed when he surfaced and stood waist-deep in water. Now, I wasn't near as old as George, and I was in pretty good shape. I knew that I could clear that canal with ease. I could continue the chase and for one fleeting second, I thought I'd give George a thrill and jump right over his head. But at the last second, I changed my mind and with one good kick I propelled myself to one side and skyward. Just like I knew I would, I sailed higher, much higher, and farther, but not much farther, than George. When I came down, I found myself standing a half-stride past George, waist-deep in water.

"I forgot to calculate the celebrating into the launch," I said and smiled sheepishly. We both laughed and waded to shore. "Whaddaya think, George? Do you think that's enough for one day?" I asked.

"Maybe we better come back tomorrow," he agreed.

We returned to Strathmore, where I got a ride to

Calgary to visit my wife and my brand-new daughter.

In Calgary, I was not a very popular fellow. I strode into the hospital like I owned the place, even though I was still soaking wet and covered with mud. The nurse, a former drill sergeant in the army, I'm sure, did not want to let me into the hospital, let alone allow me to see the baby — and she was horrified when I held her. My pride and joy, almost twelve hours old, Kelly Lea, born September 19, 1963.

*　　　*　　　*

But that was last week's lynx episode. Now George and Paddy had come calling again, ready for action. Another lynx adventure was about to unfold.

"Let's go!" yelled George. "I just got a call, there's a lynx been killing chickens north of Dalemead. Paddy's pretty excited about it."

I looked at George, then Paddy. Well, George was certainly excited. I guess Paddy could have been excited too. How could a person tell whether or not a beagle was excited, unless of course he howls "LYNX!" Right now, with those sad, deadpan eyes, he looked just like a beagle going for a car ride. I climbed into the front seat of George's car.

Our search began at a small dump site at the edge of a ravine. Dead chickens, small and large, in various stages of decomposition, were scattered among the garbage. It appeared that the lynx had been helping himself to the free handouts rather than killing his own.

The ravine was heavily treed and littered with deadfall. Poplar trees of all sizes littered the ground. This was not going to be easy.

Paddy had not yet howled when we spotted the lynx. He was a couple of hundred yards away from the buildings up the ravine. He must have heard us coming and had decided to move into cover. We had a good look at the back end of him as he walked up a deadfall. We watched as he disappeared into the foliage. We moved up to where the lynx had disappeared, and we surveyed the ravine. The beaver had obviously been there first. We stared into the worst shin tangle of trees that one man ever told another about. There didn't appear to be any way into that mess.

We walked up one side of that ravine and down the other. We scrambled over and around deadfall, working our way as far into the shin tangle as we could wherever we found the slightest opening. But to no avail. The lynx hadn't gone up a tree, at least not up any tree we could see. He had to be on the ground.

"This could very well be a problem," I mentioned to George.

"We'll get him," George replied confidently. "You go up to the top of the gully and call Paddy. I'll stay down here and let him go when you call. We'll let Paddy smoke him out."

Paddy had walked all the way around the gully with us, and his nose told us the lynx was still in the ravine. By this time, we had no doubt that Paddy would either put the lynx up a tree or drive it out the far end. At the top of the ravine I picked out a good vantage point and yelled for Paddy. I waited, then yelled again and waited some more. Nothing, not a sound, nothing stirred. I yelled again.

"He's coming, boy," George called back. "He's working his way up."

Obviously Paddy wasn't about to be hurried; he had his own agenda. It seemed like forever before I finally heard the rustling of leaves. I could hear it getting louder, coming closer, but I couldn't see it. I could feel the rush of adrenaline and anticipated seeing the lynx break into the open at any minute. It was coming right up the centre of the gully and suddenly burst into view. It was the wrong colour.

It was Paddy with his tongue hanging out who walked over, wagging his tail, and lay down at my feet.

"Paddy's here, George," I called out.

"Send him back down," George replied. "That cat's got to be in there somewhere."

Paddy was now a reluctant partner. He was tired, pooped out after all that work. I carried him down. Once more I raced to the top of the ravine. I called again and then sat down to await the arrival of Paddy, the lynx-hunting fool. Every so often I would call, and sure enough, Paddy rewarded me by walking out of the bush and lying down. He knew the routine this time and waited to be picked up.

"Let's try it once more," said George. "It's probably just a matter of Paddy not hitting the right tree. After all, boy, we know he's in there. Anyway, it can't hurt nothing, can it?"

The third time I didn't have to wait long. It seemed

like I had no sooner called for Paddy and sat down to wait when I heard it, the distinctive howl.

"AAARRRROOOO!" Paddy was baying "LYNX" loud and clear.

"Lynx!" I yelled and jumped to my feet.

"I told you he was still in there!" I heard George yell excitedly. "Keep your eyes open, boy, Paddy'll bring him right up there. He'll probably come out the top end."

"AAARRroo . . ." Paddy's voice trailed off. From the top of the ravine, it didn't sound so good.

Only seconds later I heard George's voice. It was about three octaves higher than normal.

"We should have left well enough alone, boy," George wailed, no longer excited; in fact, there was a rather dejected ring to his voice. "C'mon down here. We're finished for the day."

"AAARRrr." It was Paddy again, but his lynx call had definitely taken on a whole new tone. It was a mournful hound that was trying to bay "LYNX".

As I got near the bottom of the hill, I could see both George and Paddy. Paddy was not tired now; he was vigorously rolling in the grass and dirt and scratching his big paws over his face. Then I could smell Paddy.

"We should have left well enough alone," George wailed again.

"I should have stayed home and finished mowing my lawn," I groaned.

"Can you believe that dog came out of the bush carrying a stinking skunk?"

"George, I'd believe anything. But you know what's funny? I didn't hear him howl "SKUNK" like he howls "LYNX" when he gets the scent." I laughed.

We both stood and watched the stinking dog rolling around trying to rid himself of the smell.

"I'm not looking forward to taking him home," George said, and then burst out laughing.

"We could always leave him here and tell the guy where to find him," I suggested.

"I can't leave him here," said George. "What would we tell the guy?"

"Tell him his dumb hound dog wandered into this shin tangle and wouldn't come out."

"I think we'd better try to get this stink off before we take him back."

"What's this 'we' bit?" I asked, trying to sound very serious.

"Yeah, right," George said with a sick laugh.

"Well, suit yourself," I chuckled. "I'm glad it's your car and not mine."

We returned to town with every window in the car wide open, but there was no escaping the smell. Paddy kept rolling and rubbing himself in the back seat, every once in a while pointing his nose skyward and emitting the most mournful wail I had ever heard.

Six 48-ounce tins of Heinz tomato juice and a whole lot of scrubbing later, we stood back to allow Paddy to dry off.

"Well, boy, what do you think?" George asked as he stepped back to admire the new, clean Paddy.

"He certainly looks like Paddy to me," I assured him.

"Smell him, boy," George said. "Can you smell him?"

"I don't know," I replied. "I think my smell buds are all burned out, and I don't want to get any closer than I have to."

By the time Paddy had dried off, we could still smell skunk. I mean, the dog smelled okay but the inside of George's car left much to be desired. That was another story. We congratulated ourselves on being smart enough to deodorize the hound before returning him to his owner.

"Well, boy, we better go and face the music," George said, and he laughed. That's what I liked about my friend George—he could always find humour in any situation.

"I should really get back to mowing my lawn," I said.

After his harrowing day, Paddy was really excited to be home. He leaped out of the car and charged ahead of us through the open office door to take up residence in his favourite place, under the bench in front of his master's desk. But his master was not alone. The bench was occupied, and Paddy had no sooner dropped to the floor when one of the men on the bench jumped to his feet.

"Skunk!" he yelled. "Do you smell that? If there's one thing I hate, it's the smell of skunk."

Friend George never missed a beat.

"You know, come to think of it, I saw a dead skunk

back out on the road just this morning," George said with a straight face. "Somebody must have hit it last night."

"How'd Paddy do this time, George?" asked the owner. He was always eager to share in the glory of Paddy's latest conquests.

"Paddy? Oh . . . well, you know Paddy . . ." George sort of stumbled, searching for just the right words. "Paddy, he . . . he's just like the Mounties," George said and laughed. "He gets his . . . his man every time!"

EGG FOO Y —

"What do you say we take a little ride in the country today?" I asked Hank.

Hank, an employee in the bank in town, was really my unofficial deputy. Our wives were good friends, and whenever I had to work on weekends, which was quite often, the women would get together and Hank would accompany me on patrol. I have to admit that, for a banker, he was the best observer I ever had. It didn't seem to matter how many people were at any given place at any given time, Hank was able to document every illegal move.

It was springtime on the prairie and I was checking for beaver trappers along the irrigation canals. Hank, my right-hand man, was sitting in the passenger seat, and his sharp eyes were scanning the canal banks looking for signs of trapping activities.

"Hey, big bird!" Hank yelled as we passed a clump of willows.

"Where?" I asked and slammed on the binders. After all, an avid birdwatcher never passes up a birding opportunity.

"Right there," he stated proudly, and pointed to a bird that was flapping a hasty retreat and doing its best to keep the willows between our vehicle and itself.

"That's only a magpie, Hank," I replied with disgust.

"I know that," he said, chuckling. "I just thought I'd put a little excitement into the trip."

"That's its nest right there in the willows," I said and pointed out the big mass of sticks hanging in the trees.

"I know that, too," he said. "Hey, this will interest you. I was talking to a guy in the bank the other day and he told me Fish and Wildlife were paying five cents a pair for magpie legs. Did you know that?"

"You mean the Fish and Game Association," I replied correcting him on the name of the group.

"Yeah, whatever," he said. "Fish and Wildlife, Fish and Game, you're all the same to me."

"Come on, Hank," I protested. "I'm Fish and Wildlife, I have a uniform and work for the government. We don't pay for anything. Fish and Game is a private organization made up of sportsmen. They pay for things, like crow and magpie legs. It's part of their program to protect game birds like pheasant. I'll bet you didn't know that they even pay five cents for the eggs."

"Really?" said Hank, and the banker in him perked

right up. "Do you think there are any eggs in that nest?"

"Probably," I replied. "That's usually the reason why the old girl would be sneaking out the back door."

"Let's check and see!" he said. Man, I hadn't seen Hank that excited for a long time.

"Sure, be my guest," I said and shut off the motor.

Hank bailed out of the car and hustled right over to the willows. He stood there looking up at the magpie's nest, a mess of sticks woven into the branches of the largest willow, right smack dab in the middle of the clump. It was about ten feet above his head.

"How do we get a look at them?" he asked, standing on his tiptoes.

"The hard way," I replied and chuckled. "You have to climb up and look in."

"Hard way! Ha, that's easy," he said. "I can do that."

And do it he could. Hank was a kid again as he attacked the willows. He was as supple as a wet noodle as he snaked his way through the willows. Reaching the largest willow, where the magpie nest rested, he shinnied his way up through the tangle of branches. Hank's long arms and legs served him well, and in no time at all he reached the nest. Hank was at home in the willows. He paused for a second, resting his lanky frame, intertwined with the branches as if they were one.

"Holy mackerel!" he howled with glee when he looked in. "This thing is full of eggs! You should see all the nickels just waiting to be collected."

"How many are there?" I asked.

"I don't know, maybe twenty," he crowed.

117

I whistled. "That's a lot of eggs for one nest."

"That's a buck!" Hank yodelled. "I'll bet we could gather enough eggs to take the girls out for a good Chinese supper."

"And think of all the baby pheasants we'll be saving," I added.

"I'm gonna bring 'em down," Hank sang out happily.

"Hold it, Hank," I hastily cautioned him. "We can't do that. I'm drivin' a government vehicle. We gotta go back to town first. We can get my car, and maybe the girls would like to come out and see how hard you're gonna work to take them out for supper."

"Right on!" Hank agreed.

He clawed his way out of the willows with a big grin on his face. A face that now showed a touch of wear and tear. Not only Hank's face, but his hands and his arms all had scratches and nicks. His clothes had not fared that well either—some of the sharp branches had left permanent reminders. Hank was well on his way to being a mess, albeit a happy mess.

*   *   *

"So you boys think you can collect enough Magpie eggs to buy us supper," Mar said. Mar and Rita laughed hysterically as I turned the Volkswagen Beetle off the road onto an irrigation canal bank. "You have no idea how many eggs that will take."

"That sounds like a challenge to me. What do you think, Hank?" I replied.

"It'll be a snap," Hank said.

"This I gotta see!" Mar said scoffing at us. It would be safe to say that Mar and Rita were not as confident as Hank and I were.

It was not a long ride along the canal bank to the start of our adventure. In no time at all, I pulled up and stopped by the clump of willows to lay claim to the nickel mine, the magpie nest. Oh, the sarcastic remarks were flowing freely from the non-believers as our foursome gathered at the base of the willows.

Hank, now a scarred, veteran magpie-egg collector, ignored the comments. He paused long enough to give me a knowing smile, then he tore into the clump of willows like a man on a mission. In a matter of seconds, he was once more intertwined with the branches, looking into the magpie's nest. Hanging by one hand, he reached in and carefully removed the eggs, one at a time, and handed them down to me.

"Holy!" Mar exclaimed when Hank had finished his job. "Look at all those eggs!"

"Just about a buck's worth," Hank crowed confidently. "Now all we gotta do is find a few more nests. I believe I can already smell those sweet and sour ribs."

"Where do we get more eggs?" Rita asked. With the fruits — or should I say the eggs? — of Hank's efforts before them, the girls had a sudden change of heart. There was no denying the excitement that danced in their sparkling eyes and the unbridled enthusiasm in their voices.

"It's easy. We just drive the car until we find another

nest," I replied. "Then we send Hank up the tree again."

"What're we waiting around here for?" Mar asked. "C'mon, let's go. I'll drive."

It was then that we realized that we had forgotten to get something to put the eggs in. That was, however, a minor detail. Being the masculine types that we were, off came our shirts, and we built a nest on the back seat right between Hank and myself.

Now there was no more skepticism, and no more cheap shots. Mar and Rita had bought into our plan. Sitting in the front seats, they proved to be excellent spotters. They spotted magpie nests in places where I would never have thought to look. Those two made sure that not a single magpie nest went unsearched. It seemed like every clump of willows had a magpie nest in it, and before long the nest between Hank and me was chock full of magpie eggs. It was a day to remember, enjoying the great outdoors and the camaraderie of good friends. And the best part was still to come, a hard-earned Chinese supper.

"Do we have enough eggs for a good feed of Chinese food?" asked Rita.

"We've certainly got enough for four combination plates," I replied. I loved combination plates.

"If we get a couple more nests, we can probably get a plate of shrimp, too," Hank chimed in.

"And maybe some egg foo yong," I added.

For a banker, Hank was a devil for climbing trees. I think he had been up most of them, so I volunteered to climb to get the eggs for a plate of shrimp and for one of my favourite dishes, egg foo yong.

"Open the door and pull the seat forward," Hank yodelled to the girls. Cupped in his hands was the last batch of eggs.

"You better be careful," Mar cautioned as Hank twisted his body through the front door, and across the seat. He leaned forward and stretched his long arms out as he prepared to gently deposit the eggs on the pile.

"Careful," Mar said again. "That nest looks pretty full to me."

"This is Bob's egg foo y —" Hank started to say when suddenly his shoes slipped on the grass. Hank's feet shot out from under him, and for a second he hung in the air while a look of panic spread across his face. We all watched in horror as Hank plowed face-first into the nest of golden eggs — well, nickel eggs at least. With one slip, Hank had turned our Chinese supper into a magpie omelette, splattered all over the back seat of my Volkswagen Beetle.

"We can always go to our place for supper," Rita offered. "We can roast some wieners, or have some Kraft macaroni."

SKUNK PELTS

"Bobby," said the old fur dealer in a voice that was almost a whisper. Then he looked over his shoulder to make sure that no one was listening. I recognized the body language, the lowered voice, the glance over the shoulder. I was about to be asked for a favour, something I could provide that would be our little secret. The old fur dealer was always asking for or offering little favours. I was never sure if he was playing a game, or if he was serious.

"I'm listening." I said, I, too, looked over my shoulder, and as I had suspected, there were only the two of us in his shop. The same two who had been there for the past hour or so that I had been checking his records.

"Bobby," he asked again, his voice remaining low, "in your travels around the country, do you ever come across any skunks?"

"I beg your pardon," I said, taken aback by the odd question. "Which kind of skunks? Two- or four-legged?"

"Skunks," he whispered again. "You know, the little black animals with the white stripes." Now, everybody knew that there were skunks all over the country, in every ditch, culvert, and farmyard. There were skunks in every village, town, and city.

"You're kidding, right?" I chuckled.

"Skunks, Bobby," he said earnestly, "when you're driving through the country, do you ever come across any skunks?" I looked long and hard into the eyes of the old man. He was not kidding, he was dead serious.

"I try to avoid them if I can," I said with a grin, "but there is the odd occasion when I find myself closer than I really want to be."

"Shh! Listen, Bobby, do you hear that?" he suddenly asked. He had forgotten about the skunks, and cocked his head to one side and listened.

I held my breath and listened too, but I couldn't hear a thing. I shook my head.

"Do you hear it, Bobby?" he asked again.

"No," I replied, "I can't hear anything."

He looked quizzically at me for a second, shook his head vigorously, and then returned to the skunks.

"Bobby, do you think you could get me some skunk pelts?" he asked.

"You got to be kidding me!" I snorted. "When I see a skunk, the only thing I want to get is me a long ways away, and the quicker the better."

"I was really hopin' that you could help me out," the old man said, disappointed.

"What do you want skunk skins for?" I asked. "They're stinky as hell, and the fur isn't that great either." Actually, I was guessing on the quality of the fur, as I had never got up enough nerve to run my fingers through it to check.

"Oh, no. No, Bobby, it's a beautiful fur," the old man replied and his eyes got that look that only a fur dealer has when he encounters a piece of fur that he considers to be of a very high quality.

"Skunk fur?" I replied. "Skunk is a beautiful fur? I don't think so, my friend. It stinks to high heaven. Even if you could get someone close enough to skin it, how would you get the stink out of it?"

"Please, Bobby," he pleaded, "I got a special project I'm working on. I just need the skunks. I don't mind the smell, it doesn't bother me. They don't even have to be skinned. If you could get me the skunks, I'll skin them."

"What about the smell? How do you get rid of the smell?" I asked.

"Don't worry about that, Bobby," the old man assured me. "They won't smell a bit when I'm finished with them."

"Yeah, right!" I said and laughed. "I'm afraid not. My station wagon smells bad enough without me stuffing a bunch of skunks in it."

"I only need about a dozen, Bobby," he replied, looking at me with pleading eyes.

"I'm afraid not. I don't think I can help you," I said and shook my head. "Anyway, I think you need a trapper, my friend. I'm not a trapper."

"But you know lots of trappers, don't you, Bobby?" he asked, his voice and his eyes pleading with me.

"Yeah, I know a few. But I think they'd throw me right out of their houses if I asked them to get me a bunch of skunks," I replied. "You know more trappers than I do. Why don't you ask them?"

"Oh, I did, I asked lots of them." I watched his shoulders droop, his head dropped, and he stared at the floor for what seemed like eternity before he spoke again. "They all turned me down, Bobby."

"Gosh, I find that hard to believe," I said as sympathetically as I could. "And it's such a reasonable request, too. I just don't understand it." I shook my head sadly as I began to pack up my papers and briefcase to leave. I figured I'd had enough of skunks for one day.

"Just a minute, Bobby," the old man said and raised a finger in the air. "Before you go, can I ask you a question?"

"I'm not going to get you any skunks," I said quickly.

"Do you ever give talks to schools or to different groups?" he asked.

"I do," I replied. "In fact, I rather enjoy it."

"Do you ever take any of the pelts of fur-bearing animals with you?"

"Yes, as a matter of fact, I do. Kids love it when they can actually feel the different furs."

"Do you have a skunk pelt?" he asked, his eyes lighting up.

"I do not have a skunk pelt," I replied. "Come to think of it, I don't recall ever being asked about skunks."

"If you get me some skunks, Bobby, I'll tan one up and put a really nice backing on it so you can take it with you. You know, Bobby, kids like skunks," he said trying to entice me.

"Sorry," I replied. "No skunks."

A few days later, I stopped by a local trapper's residence to check his catch. There was a distinct odour of skunk in his yard, and an even more distinct odour of skunk on his person.

"Whew!" I whistled, and waved my hand in front of my face to get a little fresh air. "Smells like you just tangled with a skunk."

"Stupid bloody skunks!" he cursed and shook his head. "The country's full of 'em. They keep gettin' into my badger sets."

"Is that so?" I said. I had totally forgotten the old fur dealer and his request; that is, until now when I had got a good noseful of the putrid odour. "Tell me, have you ever skinned a skunk?"

"Not on your life!" he replied and snorted in disgust. "It's bad enough taking the stinking devils out of the sets."

"How many do you catch in a day?" I asked.

"Depends," he replied. "I usually get four or five. If I'm really unlucky, I get, oh . . . upwards of ten, sometimes there may be a dozen or more."

"You know, I just happen to know of a guy who's in the market for about a dozen, and right now — well, you *kind* of smell like the right sort to me," I said, and I chuckled as I waved my hand in front of my face.

"Yeah, well you go tell your friend he can have all the skunks he wants, all he hasta do is follow me around and pick 'em up."

"He might even be willing to pay you a buck or two just to bring them in to his place," I suggested.

"Can't pay me enough!" He snorted. "I don't handle skunks any more than I have to. Taking them out of the trap is really more than I want to do with them."

"Seems a shame that perfectly good pelts are going to waste when there appears to be a market, albeit a small market, for skunk pelts," I said. "Wouldn't you agree?"

He just stood and looked at me as if I had gone daft. Then he shook his head.

"I wouldn't know anything about something as complicated as that," he replied.

"I've got an idea," I said, trying to think of a way that I could get the fur dealer and the skunks together, under the same roof.

"Oh goody!" moaned the trapper. "I can hardly wait to hear this."

"You know, your truck smells a lot like skunk right now," I informed him as I walked over to his vehicle. At the back, I sort of recoiled to emphasize the degree of odour that was wafting up from the box. I waved my hand again at the fumes invading my nostrils.

"I know," he replied. "Some of my gear got sprayed this morning. I'll probably never get the bloody smell off."

"You know, if you were a conscientious man, you would just throw a dozen or so of those useless skunks into the back of the truck and haul them over to where somebody really needs them."

"In a pig's ear!" he snorted. "Once I take 'em out of a trap, I'm done with 'em. If some guy wants 'em, he can come and get 'em himself." We stood there and looked at each other for a few minutes, contemplating the world and skunks.

"I got a better idea." The trapper broke the silence. A mischievous grin spread across his face. He spoke slowly, choosing his words. "I know you're trying to help this guy out and save some skunk skins. I'll tell you what — *you* can do it! Why, I'll even help you. You be the nice guy. Tomorrow morning, you can follow me around and you pick up all the skunks you want. You can throw them in the back of that nice vehicle the government gives you to drive, and then you can take the skunks and do whatever you want with them."

"You're all heart," I said.

"Don't be too hasty, now," he cautioned. "What say we have a coffee and think on it a bit."

"The coffee part sounds fine," I said.

Two days later, the Forestry Green station wagon was following along behind the trapper's truck. Up on the luggage rack was a large box that was securely fastened down. The first badger set was not far from town, and the little black and white critter in it was not a badger. As per our agreement, the trapper took the skunk out of the trap.

"This one's not too bad," said the trapper as he

hauled the skunk out of the ditch and deposited it in the box on the roof of my Forestry Green station wagon.

"Whew! That's a crock of bull if I ever heard it!" I said, and quickly rolled up the window, but I was too late—the smell engulfed me and the inside of the vehicle.

Fifteen miles and eight skunks later, I bade the trapper good day and headed for a pre-arranged meeting with the old fur dealer.

I parked my station wagon at the back door and raced around to the front of the building. The old man stuck his nose in the air when I walked through his front door. He sniffed two or three times, testing the air.

"Whew!" snorted the old fur dealer as he fanned his hand in front of his face. "Smells a little skunky around here this morning."

"Just a little," I agreed, "but then, we were expecting that, weren't we?"

"Expecting what?" he asked, giving me a curious look.

"The skunks," I said, "we expected that they would smell a little skunky, didn't we?"

"What skunks?" asked the old fur dealer. His brow furrowed as he questioned me. The old gent seemed to be having just a wee bit of a memory lapse. I hadn't noticed that to be a problem during my previous visits. He had always been sharp as a tack when we talked furs.

"The skunks you asked for," I replied. "You do recall that you asked me if I could get you some skunks?"

"Oh yes . . . the skunks, Bobby!" He smiled as the light went on. "Can you get me some skunks? I haven't been able to convince anyone to bring some. I can skin them, you know."

"That's good," I said, smiling back at him, "because I've got some for you. They're on top of the station wagon at the back of the shop."

"You got me some skunks, Bobby?" the old man asked, hardly able to believe his ears. A big smile crossed his face and his eyes lit up like two light bulbs. He reached across the desk and shook my hand vigorously.

"I think I got eight," I said. "I sort of lost count as they were being thrown from the ditch into the box."

"Good, Bobby, good!" He laughed. "I knew I could count on you. Where are they?"

"They're in the box on the top of my station wagon at the back of your shop," I repeated.

"Can I see them, Bobby?" he asked.

"You can have every last one of them, and the box too. Grab a knife," I advised him as we walked through his shop, out the back door, and into the alley.

"Whew!" he snorted as we hit the great outdoors. "Sure smells like skunk out here."

"There is skunk out here," I reminded him. "In fact, there's eight of them. All you have to do is cut the cords and take the box off the top, and those stinkin' little black and white beauties are all yours."

"Here, Bobby," he said, holding the knife out to me. "Can you get the box down for me?"

"Nope," I said. "That was not part of our deal. I

haven't touched the box or the skunks, and I'm not about to now."

"Whoa, they sure do stink!" complained the old man as he cut the cords. The stink was a whole lot worse by the time he wrestled the box to the ground. "C'mon, Bobby, let's get inside, away from this smell," said the old man, shaking his head.

"How many more are you looking for?" I asked as the old fur dealer slammed the door shut. Then he hurried to a workbench and came back with some rags and stuffed them up against the crack at the bottom of the door.

"How many more what, Bobby?" he asked. His face was a little pale and had a questioning look.

"Skunks," I replied. "How many more skunks were you looking for?"

"Shh," he said in a low voice, holding up his hand for me to be quiet. In the stillness of his shop, we both stood very still and listened.

"Do you hear that, Bobby?" he asked me in a hushed voice.

"Nope," I replied. "I don't hear a thing."

"Listen!" he said. This time he cocked his head to one side and held a hand to one ear. We both stood and listened some more.

"Do you hear that, Bobby?" he asked again. He turned and gave me an expectant look.

"I don't hear anything," I told him.

"Just listen, right here," he said, and he pointed to the ear where he held his hand. "Do you hear that?"

"I'm afraid I don't," I said again.

131

"Listen, I've got a creek that runs right through my head," he said. "If you listen, Bobby, you can hear it."

"I'm sorry," I said, "I can't hear it."

"Bobby?" Once more his voice was lowered to a whisper. He looked over his shoulder and checked to make sure that no one else was listening. "Bobby, would you like to go fishing?"

THE BAY PARKADE

I stood at the counter and watched as Don, a Calgary city policeman and a new-found friend, finished taking the complaint. The distraught couple standing before him were the victims. Their car had been burglarized, everything had been stolen, and they were devastated. The lady cried uncontrollably as her husband provided Don with the details.

"I'm sorry," Don said sympathetically when the complaint was signed. "We'll do everything we can to get your belongings back."

"We will get them back, won't we?" the lady said, sobbing.

"We certainly hope so, and we'll do our best," Don said. "I'll get this information out to the officers on the street right away so we can give it our best shot."

"When do you think we can get our things, then?" she asked. The crying seemed to be subsiding a bit.

"Well, we don't know the answer to that. First, we

have to catch the thieves, then we have to find your property — but I promise that we'll call you as soon as we have some information," Don assured her.

"But you always catch these people and get everything back, don't you?" she asked.

"Unfortunately, no. I'm afraid we don't," Don replied. "Even when we catch the thieves, we don't always get the stuff back."

"You don't?" she asked, and the floodgates opened again.

"Sometimes we do, but not all the time. Many of the thieves sell the goods as soon as they can," Don said. "We can only hope that we get lucky and catch them first."

"Oh, no!" wailed the distraught woman. She turned to her husband. "What are we gonna do? They took everything. Everything. It's all gone. We have nothing left."

"I can assure you, we'll do everything we can to recover your goods," Don added quickly, trying once more to comfort the couple.

I felt sorry for the two of them as they turned and slowly shuffled out of the police station. Gone were the fruits of their day of shopping in the big city. Gone were the clothes for the kids. Gone were the toys. Gone were the pots and pans and tools. Gone was everything they had in the car. They reminded me of a couple of whipped dogs as they walked away.

". . . but I wouldn't hold my breath," Don added after they walked out into the street. "You know, Bob, people never learn. You don't leave anything in your car in a parkade in this city. Nothing. If you do, you're just asking for trouble. I can almost guarantee it won't be there when you get back."

"Is that right?" I asked. I was all ears.

"You can count on it," he replied.

"All parkades?" My brain was in high gear now as I listened. Don had my full attention.

"All of them," he assured me, "but the one by the Bay, where that couple parked, is especially bad for thefts."

"You don't say!" I exclaimed.

"I do say," he replied. "That parkade has to be one of the worst places in the city. Bet on it, if you leave anything in your car, anything at all, it'll be gone when you get back."

"C'mon," I kidded, "it can't be that bad."

"That bad?" he said. "Believe me, it's that bad, maybe worse." That did it—the work with the city police would have to wait. I had a more pressing errand.

"Do you guys want to excuse me for a few minutes?" I asked.

"Where you going?" Don asked.

"I've got a little errand to run," I replied. "I just remembered, my vehicle's parked in the parkade by the Bay. I'll be right back."

"Do you believe this guy?" I heard Don say to one of the other constables as I turned to leave.

"Isn't he the guy that was trained by the Mounties?" the other constable asked.

"That's right," Don replied. "That's him."

"Then I believe it," he answered, like nothing else should be expected.

"Do you need a hand?" Don called. "Can we help?"

"Not yet," I shouted over my shoulder, "but if I do, I'll be back to fill out one of those forms too. And that's another thing you can bet on."

"Okay," Don said and laughed. "If we're not here when you get back, we'll be in the coffee shop."

Laugh, boys, I thought as I hastened away, heading for the parkade. Don's words of wisdom weren't lost on me. My Forestry Green station wagon and all my government issue, with the exception of my box of shells, as well as some of my personal possessions, were in that car. I had to get to my vehicle and fast.

I shot out of the police station like a sprinter and raced down the street. I never stopped running until I reached the parkade. My Forestry Green station wagon was still there, right where I had left it. All the contents were still there. My wonky binoculars, tucked securely in the beat-up old leather case, were sitting up on the dash, partly obscured by a clipboard and a stack of papers. My ticket book, a flashlight, a pair of gloves, and my thermos were strewn about on the front seat. Everything I had was scattered around on the inside of the Forestry Green station wagon. It was just as I had left it. Untouched.

Now, there are not a lot of places in a station wagon to hide things. The only places that I knew of were under the seats. Under the seat on the driver's side went the flashlight, my ticket book, and the clipboard. Under the seat on the passenger's side went the thermos and most of the papers. Under the back seat went the beat-up old leather case, a stack of exhibit tags, and the rest of the papers.

I hid everything under the seats. Everything, that is, except my wonky binoculars that I had removed from the old leather case. I carefully wrapped the leather strap around the binoculars and I hid them up on the dash, right in the middle where they would be in plain sight. No more clipboard, no more papers to conceal them. Yes, thanks to the information I had received from my new friend Don, a little ingenious planning, and with the help of the parkade by the Bay, those non-focusing, eye-sucking headache-makers and I were about to part company. I almost, but not quite, had a tear in my eye at the thought of losing these trusted friends. Before leaving the parkade, I walked around the vehicle. Oh yes, the binoculars were in plain sight. Sitting up like a ripe apple just waiting to be picked. I turned and walked away. I was so happy, I felt like skipping, but instead, I whistled as I strolled all the way back to the police station.

"Is everything okay?" asked Don when I got back to the station.

"It sure is," I said, and chuckled, confident that someone else would soon be blessed with my wonky binoculars. "Why do you ask?"

"Just wondering," he replied. "You weren't this happy when you took off out of here like a scalded chicken."

"You know what country livin's like," I said. "Out in Strathmore, we don't even lock our doors, let alone hide everything. I just had to go and check to make sure I'd stowed all my gear out of sight."

"You really did park at the parkade, didn't you?" Don asked.

"Yeah, that's where I always park," I replied.

Don looked at me and just shook his head. "And I was just telling the guys that you seemed to be a pretty bright kid. Now you make a liar out of me. I'm telling you again, if I were you, I think I'd find a better place to park," he said. "You're asking for trouble. They'll smash a window and break into your car."

"Yeah, okay, I'll remember that for next time."

Man, but I couldn't wait for lunchtime to arrive. I was so excited at the prospect of losing those ruddy binoculars that I couldn't even eat — and that was something, for eating was always very high on my agenda. As soon as lunch was over, I bolted out of the police station and ran all the way to the parkade.

I slowed and walked towards the Forestry Green station wagon. I had visions of shattered glass lying all over the cement. I was already making up a story to tell the boys when I reported the theft. "They only took the binoculars. I was sure I had hidden everything. There was nothing in sight," I could hear myself saying.

But something was wrong. I could see the binoculars from halfway across the parkade. They were still sitting on the dash, right where I had left them, sitting right up there like an orphan, begging to be taken to a new home. I couldn't believe my rotten luck. Slowly I walked around the vehicle, inspecting the windows and the doors, but everything was exactly as I had left it. No one, it appeared, had even tried to break into the green station wagon, let alone steal my wonky binoculars.

Man, I thought, I'll do anything to get rid of those binoculars. I had tried everything I could think of in the past, and now this opportunity presented itself. It was the best chance I'd had so far. Reluctantly, I unlocked the passenger's door and rolled down the window – not all the way, just enough for an arm to be able to reach through. Well, I guess there was probably enough room for a very large arm to reach through. Maybe the open window would be enough temptation. I could only hope.

Once more I returned to the police station, but I could not concentrate on the business at hand. I had more important things on my mind. I started to think about the Forestry Green station wagon. The binoculars I had no qualms about losing, but the green station wagon – that was a whole different ball game. What would I do if it went with the binoculars? Leaving that window open was a crazy thing to do. In my mind I could see the Forestry Green station wagon pulling out of the parkade. Someone else was driving it.

By the end of the day, the Forestry Green station wagon was weighing heavily on my mind. It was causing me no end of concern. I was in such a hurry to leave, I never even said goodbye to the boys I had spent the day with. For the third time in one day, I raced away from the police station and with every step, I prayed that there had not been a theft.

I charged into the parkade and stopped. There, in the perfect spot for a prowling thief, sat my Forestry

Green station wagon. I breathed a sigh of relief. Then my thoughts turned again to the wonky binoculars. I hurried forward and my heart skipped a beat. Was something missing from the dash? Was there actually a bare spot where the binoculars had been?

"Yes!" I shouted out, for indeed there was nothing there. The dash was as bare as a baby's bottom. I was free of the old eye-suckers! Finally, after months and months of pleading for new binoculars, the Division would have to relent. New binoculars were on the horizon.

As nonchalant and cool as a country dude can be, I checked on my other gear. How much else had disappeared with the binoculars, I wondered. I checked under the driver's seat and breathed a sigh of relief — the flashlight, my ticket book, and the clipboard were still there.

"Right on," I crowed as I hauled out my gear and dumped it on the seat.

Suddenly, my mind was racing a mile a minute as I thought of how I would present my case to the police. "You were right, Don," I could hear myself saying. "Like a dummy, I parked my car in the Bay Parkade and it was broken into. Would you believe it? I've been robbed. My issue binoculars, they're gone. Stolen."

I was one happy dude, whistling as I checked under the passenger's seat. The thermos and the papers were still there. I pulled them out, but in doing so, I found a surprise. A loop of a beat-up, worn, old leather strap came out with the papers, and was now lying on the floor. I knew I hadn't put a leather strap under the seat.

Hesitantly, I gave it a very gentle tug. It was attached to something, something heavy. I got a sick feeling in the pit of my stomach. I started to pull a little harder, but the more I pulled, the more I wished I had pushed. I pulled until the pair of beat-up old wonky binoculars slid out from under the seat and lay on the floor.

I could have cried as I picked up my wonky binoculars. I walked to the edge of the parkade and looked out across the city at the banks of the Bow River. Then I slowly lifted the binoculars to my eyes and trained them on the distant grassy slopes. In a matter of seconds I could clearly see the error of my ways. Those lenses sucked at my eyes until they began to water. Then a shooting pain, like a jagged bolt of lightning, slashed through my left eye. And a throbbing headache began to pound in my temples.

Oh Bob, I moaned to myself, why do you put yourself through all this misery, why don't you just drop them to the street below?

THE CHICK IN THE FANCY CAR

The scene could well have been the setting for an action-type Hollywood movie. There were red flashing lights everywhere. A highway patrol cruiser was parked right in the middle of the Trans Canada Highway. Cars were parked in the ditches on both sides of the highway. Cars lined the exit leading into the weigh scales. Cars were strategically parked around the weigh scales building. And most of these cars were decked out with red flashing lights and flashing park lights. They belonged to enforcement officers — Fish and Wildlife officers, Royal Canadian Mounted Police officers, town policemen, and Highway Traffic officers. There were also numerous biologists and Ducks Unlimited personnel.

This was the opening weekend of the pheasant season in southern Alberta, and all agencies were gathered for a massive check station. The primary purpose of the check was biological, but for eight hours everybody travelling past that point on Highway 1 would be stopped. Drivers who were not obviously hunters were waved through the check point. However, as I had often been told as a youth, believe only half of what you see.

It was just past sunset when, for some unknown reason, the RCMP constable out on the point on the highway directed a dark-coloured, spiffy new car into the check station.

"We'll have to get him off the point," I muttered to one of the biologists, when I looked at the driver. "He's obviously been standing there too long, or he's losing his sight." The driver, a young lady, was dressed to the nines, and it didn't take much imagination to know that she was not a hunter.

I stepped back and waved her through, but she didn't move. She rolled down the window and smiled at me.

"You didn't have to stop," I called to her. "This is a hunter check station. You can just drive on through."

"But I'm a hunter," she said.

"You are?" I asked. "You don't look like a hunter!"

"I know," she cooed.

"Well, then, you just pull over in that line right there," I said. "Someone will be with you in a moment."

"Thank you," she said, smiled sweetly, and drove ahead.

"I guess I better cancel the change on the point," I said to the biologist. "Obviously that's one smart Horse Cop out there."

A few minutes later, I had a visitor.

"I think you better come and check out the chick in the fancy car, boy!" George said, and struggled to stifle a laugh.

"Why's that?" I asked. "You got a bird you can't identify?" It was the first time that George had ever asked for assistance in checking anyone.

"You just go and check it out for yourself," he said. "I'm not touching that one."

"Okay," I said. "You direct traffic till I get back."

I walked over to the vehicle. I tapped on the window, and the well-dressed lady looked up and smiled. It was not that cold but she had the heater on, and the hot air loaded with perfume hit me like a blast furnace when she rolled down the window. Of the thousands of hunters I had checked, there had been a lot who smelled, but never like that.

"I'm sorry, ma'am, this is really a hunter check. You didn't have to stop," I said. "You can just take that lane and follow it back onto the highway."

She batted her eyes at me, then gave me a knowing sweet smile. No wonder George had left in such a hurry, I thought to myself.

"Oh, but Officer, I am a hunter," she cooed softly.

"I'll just bet you are," I said, and chuckled to myself. "I'll just bet you are."

"So which nice man is going to check me?" she asked, batting her eyes once more.

"I guess that would be me. I can check you," I replied. "Have you been hunting this weekend?"

"Yes, I have," she replied. She looked very pleased

144

to have been able to finally answer that question.

"Good," I said. "And did you have any luck?"

"Oh yes, I did," she replied happily.

"Good for you," I said. "And of course you have a hunting licence, don't you?"

"Of course I do," she replied. "I've got it right here, but I did show it to the other gentleman. I hope that was okay?"

"That's fine," I assured her. "My partner's a little shy, sometimes." George, I thought to myself, I'm going to get you for this.

I couldn't help but notice the fingernail polish, as bright red fingernails opened up a purse that could have passed for a small suitcase. At times it seemed that she had both hands and her head in there as she rummaged around in the depths of the thing. After some time, to my amazement, she actually produced a licence.

"Well," I said sheepishly, after I checked her licence, a valid bird game licence, "you certainly fooled me. You don't look like any hunter I've ever checked."

"Oh, I'm not your ordinary hunter," she said, and gave me a knowing smile, "but I am a hunter and I've even got my birds with me. They're in the trunk. Would you like to see them, too?"

"Let me guess," I mumbled. "My partner has already had a look at them. Right?"

"Yes, he did. But you can look at them, too, if you'd like?" she said proudly.

"Absolutely," I replied. "I'd love to."

"That other man was so nice, he even told me what

my birds were," she added.

"There was never a doubt in my mind that he would," I replied.

I watched her get out of her car. She wore a fancy white blouse with bouffant sleeves. A silk scarf was tied in a loose knot around her neck. Her skirt, a tight black job, came about halfway to her knees. And her shoes had spikes about three inches high. Wait till I get my hands on George, I thought, as I followed the lady to the trunk of her car. She popped the trunk open and proudly stepped aside.

"Oh, my goodness," I barely whispered when I looked into that trunk. "You really are a hunter, aren't you?"

"Yes, I am," she chirped proudly.

"And a good shot too, I might add," I muttered. "Why, I'd even say you were a regular Annie Oakley."

"Uh-huh," she said and then pointed her index finger at me like a pistol. "Bang. Bang!" She chuckled.

"Did . . . did you shoot these, all by yourself?" I asked.

"Well, not all by myself. I'm not really that good a shot," she said, and giggled. "I was with a hunting party. They gave me most of the birds to bring back. But we did pretty good, didn't we?"

"You certainly did," I responded as I sorted through the birds and counted them. "Just how many people were in this hunting party of yours?"

"I'm sorry, I can't say," she cooed coyly. Then she winked at me. "I was sworn to secrecy."

"I see," I said. "That's all well and good when you're playing games. Unfortunately, this is not a game. With all these birds, you're way over your legal limit. Right now, you're in some serious trouble. I'm afraid you are going to have to break that oath. As it stands right now, you have several possessions of pheasant and ducks. I'm going to have to have the names of everybody that was in your hunting party so that I can check them out,"

"Oh no, I can't tell you who I was with," she replied very seriously. "That just wouldn't be right."

"Let me explain it to you this way," I said. "Right now you have way too many birds in your possession. If you don't tell me who you were with, I'm going to charge you with illegal possession. I'm also going to seize all the birds and your car."

"You . . . you mean you can seize my car?" she asked, sounding somewhat surprised.

"Yes, I can," I assured her.

"I didn't know that you could take my car." She looked as if she was ready to cry.

"Yes, I can seize anything that is used in the commission of an offence. And this is a very flagrant violation," I told her. "Now then, if you'd like to tell me who you were hunting with."

"If I tell you, you can't tell anyone else," she whispered in a pleading voice.

"I'll tell you what I'll do," I said. "You tell me who you were with, and I'll check them out. If everything is legal, then you're free to go and no one will be the wiser. However, if everything is not legal, then I'll be

147

laying charges against whoever is responsible for all this. As far as telling anyone, that's up to you; you can tell anyone you want. If there are any charges that result from this, I just give the circumstances to the court. How does that sound, fair enough?"

"Oh no!" she wailed, and started to cry. "Oh please, you can't tell anyone. I'll die if anyone finds out. Promise me you won't tell, please."

"Only the magistrate," I replied.

After a short cry and repeated requests that I not tell anyone, she finally agreed to give me the names of her hunting partners. Very hesitantly she offered a name. I wrote it down and waited for more. But she was silent. She didn't utter another word.

"Are you going to tell me who else was in the party?" I asked.

"Th-That's all," she sobbed, "there were just the two of us." Then she started to cry again.

"Who is this guy, and where can I find him?" I asked. I watched and waited for the flood of tears to subside. "Whenever you're ready. I've got all night."

"I work for him. He's my boss," her voice was almost inaudible as she looked up at me with pleading eyes. The tears had not done much for her makeup, I thought, looking at smudged mascara and streaky cheeks.

"Well, I can certainly see why you don't want me to tell anybody," I sighed. "Now, where do I find your boss at this time of night?"

"He's got his own car. He was going to leave the motel after I did and follow me to make sure I got home okay. He should be driving right by here," she blubbered.

"Do you know what kind of a car he's driving?"

"Yes, it's a dark-coloured car, something like mine, I think, but I don't know what kind. I don't know anything about cars."

"Well, I guess we'll just wait until he arrives. Are you okay to drive your car over here by the building?" I asked.

She nodded and I pointed to where I wanted her to park, around the far side of the building, out of sight of the oncoming traffic. I told her to stay there until I returned.

I raced to the Mountie on point and told him to start checking driver's licences, that I was looking for a lone male in a dark-coloured car; I gave him the name. About every ten minutes I checked in on the little gal. She sat alone and sobbed to herself.

I was beginning to think that the other half of the hunting party had got by before we knew of him when, lo and behold, I got a call from the Mountie. Sure enough, he had a dark-coloured car with a lone male occupant pulled over to the side.

"What's this all about?" snarled the driver as I walked up.

"Good evening, sir," I greeted him. "I was just wondering how your day was."

"My day was great," came the no-nonsense response. "What is this, a game check?"

"That it is, sir," I replied. "That it is. And how about you, doing a little hunting this weekend?"

"Not me," he said. Obviously the very thought offended him. "If you're looking for hunters, you've got the wrong guy. I'm just returning from a business trip. Now if you're finished with me . . ."

"Not quite, sir," I smiled back at him. "I have it on good authority that you were hunting. Now, if you don't mind, I'd just like to have a look in your trunk. Would you open it, please."

"Like hell I will. I'm not hunting and you've no right to stop me, let alone search my car."

"You may just want to think about that for a minute, sir," I cautioned him. "You see, I have a little lady parked over by the weigh scales and she tells me—"

"Oh my Lord," he moaned. He placed both hands on the steering wheel and dropped his head on his arms. "What else did she tell you?"

"Probably a whole lot more than I needed to know," I replied.

"She didn't."

"She did," I assured him. "She also told me that you shot most of the birds she has in her vehicle. Now, would you like to show me your hunting licence and open your trunk?"

"Okay," he said, and his whole attitude changed. Suddenly, he was in complete control. "So, what do you think you're gonna do about it?"

"I need to know who's gonna claim ownership of the birds in her car."

"Yeah, I am. Most of them are mine," he said.

"In that case, I'll need a statement from you to that effect, and then I'm going to charge both of you for

150

being over possession of game birds. Now, if you'd just pull your car over to where your secretary is parked, we can finish this up and you can be on your way."

I was feeling pretty confident now. This was a good case, one that could make a young officer's career. I would have to remember to thank George when this was over, I thought, and congratulated myself.

"Let's cut the crap," the guy said. He was back to his indignant self. "You're not going to charge anybody!"

"I'm not?" I replied, taken aback by this outburst. "Why is that?"

He sneered at me. "Do you know so-and-so in Edmonton.?"

"No, not personally, but I know of him," I replied, and the name certainly sent a shiver down my spine. He was one of the Powers That Be. In fact, he was even bigger than the Powers That Be. I had it on good authority that whenever he took an interest in a Fish and Wildlife matter, the officer came out second-best. I knew officers who had told me that they had had their tails twisted by this man. And I could feel the fear that was in their voices when they assured me it had not been a pleasant experience. Rumour had it this man considered Fish and Wildlife people to be the lowest form of humanity, the bottom of the barrel — and to find a Fish and Wildlife officer, one had but to lift the barrel and look underneath.

"He's a good friend. My neighbour, in fact," snarled the man. "And as soon as I get back home, I'll have this piddly thing and you squashed so fast it'll make your head spin, sonny boy." Then he smiled a very unfriendly smile.

"Whoa now, wait up a minute," I quickly replied as another shiver shot up my spine. "Let me think for a minute."

And think I did. I thought about what I was gonna do with an arrogant hunter, his mistress, and a trunk full of illegal birds. I thought about the older officers as they relayed their stories about laying tickets on the wrong guy. I thought about my career crashing to a sudden halt at a check station on the Trans Canada Highway. This case was not a career-maker; it was a nightmare, a career-breaker. It was a no-winner. No matter what I did, I couldn't win.

But even so, there was no way I could allow him to leave with all those birds.

"I just can't let you drive away from here with all those birds. But I-I'll tell you what I can do," I stammered. "For now, I'm gonna keep both your and the lady's licences. I'll put the birds in my car, and we'll all go back into Strathmore. You folks can go to the coffee shop across the street, and I'll make a couple of phone calls. Hopefully, we can get this all straightened out tonight. It'll save all of us a lot of time and grief. Does that sound okay to you?"

"Smart kid," he said and chuckled smugly. "I can live with that."

"Good, I'll just get the birds and put them in my car. You two can follow me back into town." I had absolutely no idea what I was going to do when I got back to town.

"Is it okay if we leave one car here, rather than

driving them both back and forth?" he asked.

"Absolutely. I was going to suggest that myself," I purred. Suddenly, butter wouldn't melt in my mouth. I was the picture of concern, and as obliging as all get-out.

Back in Strathmore, I pointed out the coffee shop. "Why don't you two go over and have a coffee. In the meantime, I'll make the calls. You come back in, say, a half-hour. Hopefully I'll have this all straightened out by then. Is that okay?" I asked.

"Hmpf!" He sneered at me as they walked away. I had the feeling that he, too, felt that Fish and Wildlife officers lived under barrels.

My first call was not to the Powers That Be, but to the local magistrate. I was in a bind, and I needed some good counselling.

*   *   *

"Well, have you made that call?" asked the hunter, scowling at me as he walked into the Fish and Wildlife office. He gave the person in the room with me no more than a passing glance. "I'm in a hurry. I've got a long way to go and I want to get going."

"I-I have," I replied, my knees knocking so hard I thought I might collapse.

"Order . . . order in court," I called out as loud as my voice would carry.

"What the hell is this?" said the surprised man.

"It's . . . it's a court of law," I replied. "His Worship, Magistrate Ferguson, presiding."

"Please stand." The words were wasted, since everyone except the magistrate was already standing. "This court is now open in the name of Her Majesty the Queen. You may be seated."

"What is this? What's going on here? This is no courtroom! It's . . . it's a bloody game warden's office!" the very surprised well-dressed hunter barked, looking first at me, then at the magistrate.

"Order in the courtroom!" growled the magistrate. "Can I have the charges, Officer?"

He called both names. The accused, both of them, stood there with their mouths open. Then the young lady started to cry, and more streaks appeared on her cheeks. The middle-aged man stood there in stunned silence. This was not the reception that he had prepared himself and the little lady for.

The magistrate read the first charge to the weeping lady. "Illegal possession of wildlife: to wit, pheasant. Do you understand the charge?" he asked her.

She nodded her head, indicating a "Yes".

"I'm sorry, I didn't hear you. Could you speak a little louder, please?" asked the magistrate.

"Yes!" she wailed.

"'Yes' what? 'Yes' you can speak up, or 'Yes' you understand the charge?" the magistrate asked.

"Yes, I understand the charge," she sobbed.

"Good, and how do you wish to plead to this charge?"

"Guilty," she almost whispered.

Then he read the next charge.

"Do you understand the charge?" His Worship

asked a very pale man who could not believe what was happening.

"Yes, I understand the charge," came the reply.

"How do you plead to the charge?"

"Guilty."

"Could you please read the circumstances, Officer?"

It was my turn to be surprised. I had honestly expected that both would enter pleas of not guilty.

I related all of the circumstances and identified the additional charges that could have been slapped on. I even mentioned the gentleman's threat of having the Powers That Be descend on me from great heights. I concluded by requesting the Court to take into serious consideration all of the circumstances, particularly the gentleman's conduct, and asked for a penalty befitting his unthinkable actions.

When I finished, I looked at the accused. The lady was still sniffling. The guy was staring daggers at me; there was pure hatred in his face. I wanted to see his eyes when the magistrate threw the book at them. Well, particularly at him.

The magistrate then politely asked if either of them wished to say anything in their defence. Neither did.

"Twenty-five dollars, and costs on each count," ordered His Worship, "and all seizures forfeited to the Crown." With the passing of the sentence, there was suddenly a whole lot of disbelief in the makeshift courtroom.

"Oh no, you can't do that!" the lady suddenly howled and burst into tears.

"That — that's it," stammered the surprised man and

he quickly reached for his wallet.

"What?" I howled, not believing my ears.

"Not my car!" wailed the distressed lady. "Please, sir, you can't take my car."

"Car," repeated the magistrate. He, too, was surprised by the sudden chain of events his decision was producing. Realizing that he had just forfeited all the seizures, he had a serious look on his face when he turned to me and asked, "Officer, did . . . did you seize this woman's car?"

"T-twenty-five dollars!" I sputtered and glared at the magistrate in disbelief. "Y-you only gave them the minimum!"

This was unbelievable. Who in his right mind but a game warden would put his job on the line for a twenty-five-dollar fine. A Fish Cop, I thought, only a Fish Cop.

"Officer Adams!" roared the magistrate. His voice reverberated throughout the building, as he struggled to regain control of his courtroom. Then he repeated his question. "Did you seize this lady's car?"

"No—no, Your Worship," I replied, feeling like a whipped dog. "I didn't, but I'm thinking that I should have."

"THERE'S A MILLION GEESE!"

"Good day, sir," I greeted the farmer who had stomped through the door and now stood at my counter. "How's the harvest coming along?"

"Oh, I suppose it's fine," he replied. "It's fine, that is, if you're a goose."

"That's a good one," I said and chuckled. I hadn't heard that expression before, but then I had come to expect some good lines from time to time. "I take it that your harvest is finished, then. How was your crop this year?"

"No, I'm not finished. And yes, I did have a good crop before the geese moved in. They fixed that in short order. Now I need a permit to fix those dang geese," he declared as he leaned over my counter and stared me straight in the eye.

It was not unusual to get a request to shoot geese on

a permit. It was, however, highly unusual for the request to be successful, and I thought the timing was a little odd. It was perfect harvest weather, and harvesting in the Strathmore area was in full swing. What was unusual about this request was that the farmer had personally taken time off to come to the office for a permit. This just didn't happen when the weather was good and there was still crop in the field. The priority was always to get the crop off.

"Really,? I said. "You've got a few geese, have you?"

"A few!" He snorted. "There's a million of 'em. If I don't get 'em out of my field, there'll be nothing left for me."

"I see," I said. "You know, that we don't issue permits to shoot geese, but I can give you a permit to scare the little devils. How does that sound?"

"Nope, that's not good enough," he stated emphatically. "I don't need no permit to scare 'em. I need a permit to shoot 'em."

"How about a Zon Gun?" I asked. This was a proven way of scaring geese out of a field. "Have you tried using a Zon Gun? You know, they do make a big bang and they're pretty effective when it comes to scaring geese."

"Tried Zon Guns," he replied. "They didn't work."

"What about scarecrows. Have you tried scarecrows?"

"I've tried everythin'!" he said, getting a little agitated. Then he leaned across the counter a little farther and glared at me. "I told you, I tried everythin'. Nothin' works. There's a million geese feedin' in my field and I can't get them out!"

"I'm sorry," I responded, "but you know I just can't give you a permit to shoot them."

"Well then, I'm servin' notice on you right now, I'm gonna shoot 'em, with or without your stupid little permit!" He stormed. "An-an' I wanna tell you somethin', just so's you know. I've been feedin' your geese all my life and I've never shot one. But this year, I've about had it. They've been in my barley now for over a week, they've just about eaten the entire crop."

"You mean the whole field?" I asked. Man, I could sympathize with him for losing his whole field of barley. I'd be mad as a hornet, too, I thought.

"The whole field," he repeated. We stood there silently for several seconds.

"And I suppose you've tried chasing them out of the field?" I asked. "That's one method that usually works on geese, you know. Geese are pretty spooky at the best of times."

"Tried chasing 'em out with my truck," he assured me. "The boys just about used up all my gas chasin' them things around the field. They just fly up and land a short distance away."

"You don't say!" I declared. "You know, I've seen ducks do that, but never geese. Sounds to me like you must have one heck of a crop of barley this year."

"Well, I did before the geese came. Like I said, they're in there by the millions and I haven't been able to get 'em out. The only thing I haven't tried is shootin' 'em out. And I'm gonna do that in the morning, with or without your permit."

"I'll tell you what I'll do," I proposed. "Why don't I come out to your place this afternoon. If the geese are as bad as you say, I suppose I could make an exception and issue you the permit."

"That'll be fine," he said and laughed happily. "The geese are usually in the field by four. Just stop by the house; we'll be there then. Oh, by the way, after you give me the permit, why don't you stop around in the morning. I'm gonna get some boys to give me a hand shooting. Once the geese are gone, I figure we'll take some pictures and have breakfast. You're welcome to join us. I'll bet the boys would get a kick out of watchin' the local game warden shoot a goose in our field."

"I'll be there at four," I assured him, "And I'll make sure I have my permit book with me."

"You know, some of the boys been saying bad things about you. They said you was a real hard nose, that you'd even pinch your own mother," the farmer said. Then he gave me a knowing grin and chuckled. "Well, I guess they just don't know you."

"I guess you never know, do you?" I said.

I arrived at the farm shortly after three and was met by the whole family. They took turns impressing upon me the need for a permit to shoot the geese and save the crop. We toured the field, which had a heavy swath lying in it. On a small knoll visible from the farm buildings we came to the damaged area. Here there were no swaths. The geese had done an excellent job of shelling out the grain. There were goose droppings and feathers everywhere I looked. I could not deny that geese were the culprits.

"Why don't we go in the house," the farmer suggested. "The coffee pot's always on, you know."

"No thanks," I said. "I'll just stay out here and watch for the geese." It seemed like nobody wanted a cup of coffee, and we all stayed outside.

"You know, I don't recall seeing any Zon Guns or scarecrows out there," I said. "Did I miss them?"

"No," replied the farmer. "We're gonna start combining tomorrow, right after the shoot, so I had the boys pick 'em up this mornin'. Why?"

"Oh, I don't know. I just thought you'd want to keep trying to scare the geese. That's why."

"Nothin' works," he replied. "I've tried everything and nothin' works. I thought I might as well pick 'em up before we start."

"I see." I couldn't argue with his logic.

Right on time, just like the farmer said, the first small flock of geese appeared on the horizon. Long before they were even close to the field, another flock could be seen trailing in the distance. The first flock came in low over the fenceline and headed directly for the knoll. There was no circling, as geese normally do when approaching a field. These birds came right in, set their wings, and dropped to the ground. The second flock followed closely behind. Suddenly, as far as I could see there were flocks of geese. There were flocks of all sizes, and they were all making a beeline straight for the barley field in their quest for food. In no time flat, the knoll was black with geese.

"What did I tell ya!" said the farmer. "Have ya seen enough yet?"

I whistled. "Man, that's a lot of geese. That's as many as I've ever seen in one field at one time."

The farmer chuckled, and said, "I guess, you can start writin' anytime."

We both stood there for a few more minutes watching the birds. Watching flock after flock streaming into the field. Then I walked over to my car, got in behind the wheel, and started the motor. The farmer had been so intent on watching the birds that he didn't see me walk away. You could have knocked him over with a goose feather when I drove past him and out into his barley field.

In the rear-view mirror I could see him waving and running after me as I drove towards the knoll and the feeding geese. I followed the tracks we had made earlier when he was showing me the damage.

As my car raced across the swaths, the geese lifted their heads to look at me. Their long necks seemed to get even longer as the vehicle bore down on them. Then it was just like he said, the geese raised their wings and lifted into the air and flew up. But this time they didn't just fly a short distance — they kept flapping their wings frantically as they flew higher and higher and farther and farther. In only a few minutes, I had accomplished what the farmer and his boys had not been able to do. There was not a goose left in his field. I stopped the car on the knoll and watched as the rapidly retreating birds headed for parts unknown. I felt quite proud of myself, for I had single-handedly solved his problem.

When I drove back into the yard, I could tell that the family were quite impressed with me. I stepped out of the car with a big grin on my face.

"You . . . you idiot!" roared the farmer as I stepped out of my car. "What do you think you're doin'?"

I looked at him in utter amazement. Could I have misread the situation? This was one irate farmer. He was not at all happy with my work.

"I-I think I just solved your problem," I replied hesitantly. "I don't think those geese will be eating any more of your crop." I looked back out at the barley field. "Look, the geese are gone. There's not a goose to be seen anywhere. They won't be back. Your boys probably didn't think of driving straight at them like I did. You know, if you wanna chase geese, you gotta have the right technique."

But my comments just infuriated him more. His face had turned a beet red. His mouth was moving up and down, and spittle was flying. He wanted desperately to say something, anything. I had this feeling he didn't want to congratulate me, but could not manage a word through his quivering lips.

"You . . . you ruined everything!" one of his boys finally blurted out, his eyes filling with tears. "You knew, I'll bet that you knew *Otis Outdoors* was coming to our farm to shoot geese tomorrow, and now . . . now you've ruined everything. You've scared all the geese away."

"Otis Outdoors!" I exclaimed. Now, this was a little revelation that really caught me off guard. "Isn't that the . . . isn't he that guy on television? You know, the guy with the hunting and fishing show."

"Shaddup!" the farmer suddenly yelled at his boy.

163

It appeared that he had finally found his voice.

"You promised, Dad," the kid whined. "You promised. You said if we could get a permit to shoot the geese, we'd all be on television. Now *Otis Outdoors* won't come 'cause . . . 'cause there's no geese to shoot, and it's all your fault. I warned you, Dad, I warned you. I said, 'Don't trust that game warden, Dad,' I said. 'He's a miserable guy and . . . and he'd pinch his own mother.'"

"HOW CAN A MAN LIVE ON THIS?"

As a young Fish Cop, I had a love-hate relationship with payday. On one hand, I loved payday. It was the one day of the month when, for a few brief moments, I felt like I owned the world. Well, actually, I may have felt that I owned just a part of it. A very small part at that. On the other hand, I also hated payday. It was the one day of the month that I got to stand in line at the local bank. Clutching my paycheque in my hot little hand, I loathed walking in and looking at the lineups, and then lining up only to pay all my hard-earned money to my creditors. Which lineup was moving the fastest? Everyone in line would turn and watch, to see which line I chose, and whether my choice would be better than theirs. Really, it didn't matter which line I chose, one was no better than the other. I always picked the shortest line, and each time I would curse, for there was a reason it was the shortest—it was the one that moved slower than the rest. Then I had to stand and wait patiently for the teller to call.

"Next, please."

It was always satisfying if I could arrange it so that I was speaking with someone behind me in line; then the teller would have to call twice.

"Next, please," she would call out, her voice a tad louder, with more than just a tinge of annoyance in it. I considered this a sort of payback for having to wait so long.

"I'm sorry," I would warble as I signed my cheque in front of her, "but you know, I haven't seen old Joe for quite a spell and I, well, I guess I got a little carried away. Did I keep you waiting long?"

The friendly lady would hand me my few bills, which I would deliberately count out while she waited. Then, if everything looked like it was in order, I would hand her back five dollars and ask her to put it into my savings account. I would have liked to put in ten percent of my paycheque, but five dollars was even more than I could afford, and I knew that I would take out most of it before the end of the month.

The year was 1965 and the game-bird hunting season was in full swing. I had been out in the field since daybreak, checking hunters that were swarming over the country. Many who had left the fields, sloughs, and lakes were now driving the roads; road hunting was a favourite pastime, and it was an excellent time for a Fish Cop to be in the outdoors checking hunters. However, not on this day.

My paycheque should have been in on Thursday, but as was so often the case, it was delayed in the mail. Although I never understood the reasons, I had come to accept the fact that there would be delays. I don't know how they managed it, but anything that a person needed by a certain date, the Post Office could be counted on to delay. My creditors did not understand, nor did they accept; in fact, they did not care about the reason. I owed them for services rendered, and they expected their money at the end of the month. The delays were my problem, not theirs. Fail to pay the bills and there would be no more credit. No more credit meant one sure thing—a very sparse larder at the Adams household.

I was anxious to get back into the field, but first things first. I had to get my cheque and pay my bills. I sped into town and raced into the post office.

"Hey, look at this!" I said, acting surprised, when the postmistress handed me the envelope.

"What's that?" she asked.

"My cheque!" I warbled. "Now I can live for another month."

"I thought your paycheque came in yesterday," she said, with a curious sort of look on her face as she looked at the envelope.

"Yeah, I thought so, too. It was supposed to," I replied, "but it didn't, did it?"

"I'm sure the rest of the government cheques came in yesterday," she said and shook her head. It appeared to be a mystery that was beyond her, too.

"Makes you wonder, doesn't it?" I said and shook

my head. "It really makes you wonder."

Clutching my paycheque, I raced out of the post office. Across the street I ran and barged through the door into the bank. I stopped abruptly. Reality set in when I encountered the sea of humanity. It seemed that there were a good many others whose government paycheques had not arrived on time. I think every one of them had beaten me to the bank.

"Why would anyone in his right mind bust his butt to get across the street, only to stand and wait," I muttered.

"Because the bank's only open from ten to three," growled the guy ahead of me.

There were three wickets in the old bank, but today there was only one teller and one line, which wound its way from the wicket back to the door.

"This is one part of payday that I could very easily do without," I grumbled.

"Hmph," grunted the guy ahead of me.

As usual on payday, the lineup moved slowly. Today, however, because I was anxious to get back to the field, it was moving at a snail's pace. I had been in the lineup a long time and was about halfway through when someone touched my arm.

"Hello, Mr. Adams," said a meek, quiet voice.

I turned to see a man that I had met some two years earlier and I had come to know quite well. His name had been given to me as someone who was down on his luck and could use a little help.

"Hey, my friend," I greeted him, "how are you today?" My friend, too, relied on a government cheque to feed his family. His cheque came from a different department of the government, but it was obviously a day late as well.

"Oh, not so well," he replied. "I was wondering if it would be all right if I stood beside you? You know, it kills me to stand too long, and the lineup's almost out the door."

"Yeah, I know," I said. "It feels like I've spent most of the morning in here myself."

"Would it be all right if I joined you?" he asked again.

"I don't see any reason why not. In fact, you can even have my spot." I said, stepping back to allow him to slip into the line."

"Hey, back of the line, freeloader!" someone yelled.

"I know standing is difficult for you." I spoke very loud so that everyone could hear me. "You know, I think maybe I'll stand here with you, just in case you need some help."

"No. No, that's okay, I'll be fine," he responded meekly.

"Hey, I know what I can do for you, my friend. I can take you right up to the front of the line," I barked in my loudest voice for the lip at the back of the line to hear. "What do you say, wouldn't you like to get to the front of the line and get your banking done so you don't have to spend all day in here?"

"No," he replied quickly. "I'm okay right here. This is just fine. Thank you."

"Always glad to be of assistance," I trumpeted loudly, then turned to look at the scowling faces behind me. "Yessiree, always glad to help. You just let me know if there's anything else I can do for you."

"Well," he said, "I was just wondering if you've had a busy fall."

"Oh yeah, it's been a busy one all right," I replied. "There's a ton of bird hunters out there. In fact, that's where I should be right now."

"How about deer hunters? Are there any deer hunters?" he eagerly inquired.

"I certainly hope not," I said. "The deer season doesn't open until next month."

"I was hoping that you might have a little extra deer meat," he said.

"I know," I mumbled. I didn't like to talk about forfeited meat, but he certainly had good reason to inquire, I thought. After all, deer meat was the reason that I had been introduced to him and certain others in town. They were needy families, and to some, deer meat was a way of supplementing the meagre pittance they existed on.

During the deer season, I came into possession of many illegal deer. Arrangements had been made with care workers who would identify the needy, and with a local butcher who cut, wrapped, and froze the meat. The meat would then be doled out until it was gone. I recognized that it wasn't much, but it helped, and this man in particular was always so happy whenever there was venison available. Unable to work, or hunt for himself, he never missed an opportunity to inquire as to the state of the government larder. In the past couple of years, I had given him many, many pounds of venison.

"I hope you'll remember my family again this year," he asked.

"You can count on it," I assured him in a low voice.

"Well, I can't thank you enough," he said. "My family really counts on that meat. We wouldn't be able to make ends meet without it."

"I'm glad I can help," I assured him.

The conversation was beginning to make me feel more than just a little uncomfortable. His family, a wife and a couple of kids, was not too different from mine. Watching him almost grovelling in front of me, I suddenly thought of my own family, my wife and two little girls. I had a good job, and even if the Post Office couldn't get my cheque to me on time, I always knew it was coming. My family was happy and secure, not having the worry of where our next meal was coming from. Strange, I thought, how someone far less fortunate than yourself had the ability to humble you. Suddenly, I felt a twinge of guilt. For the past several years, I had enjoyed continuous employment; I didn't have lots of money, but I had enough so that I never worried about my next meal. Now, here I was in a crowded bank and I was feeling uncomfortable about my success. I found myself praying, praying for the line to speed up, praying to get out of the bank. Man, I needed to escape from this place.

"Just look at this, Mr. Adams," he suddenly blurted out. "This is all they give me."

"Uh, no, it's okay," I mumbled.

This day was rapidly going from bad to worse. I had been feeling bad enough, just standing there thinking

171

about the puny amount of venison I was giving him. I really didn't need to know how much money he was getting. I turned my head, not wanting to look at the cheque that he was holding out for me to see.

"You're lucky," he continued. "You don't know what it's like not to have a job, not to be able to work. Here, take a look at this, I want you to see what they give me to live on. I'm expected to raise my kids, to feed and clothe them, on this. Just look."

"Yeah, it's gotta be tough," I mumbled. "I-I, can only imagine how tough it is." I had gone beyond feeling uncomfortable, I was embarrassed. I hated this type of confrontation, watching this man bare his soul like this. Now I wished I had forgotten about my creditors, taken my cheque, and gone back on patrol.

"Just look at this," he demanded and, with a trembling hand, thrust his cheque in front of my face. "Can you tell me how a man can live on this? My family, they . . . they're living in poverty."

I avoided eye contact with him. I had a sudden urge to bolt from my place in the line, charge out of the bank, race across the street, get in my green station wagon, and speed out of town. But I couldn't help seeing the numbers written on the cheque, nor I'm sure could several of the people standing behind me. I don't know what they thought, but I was stopped cold. My eyes were drawn like a magnet to the numbers, and I stared in disbelief. It was unbelievable. The amount on his cheque was for . . . for well over three hundred dollars.

His family was the same size as mine, and he had to care for them for the next month with the money he would receive from that cheque. Of course, with deer season coming up, he knew he could expect help from the local Fish Cop.

"Can you believe that?" he asked.

"No, actually I can't," I replied. Now I was both furious and embarrassed. "I wish they'd hurry up," I muttered.

It took forever for my friend to reach the teller. I stood impatiently and waited. I listened to first the teller and then my friend count out his money.

"Thank you for being so kind to me, Mr. Adams," he said as he turned away from the wicket. "You won't forget my family when you get some deer steaks, now, will you?"

"Oh, you can count on me," I mumbled and stepped up to the teller. I pushed in close to the wicket. I had always been a little self-conscious about the size of my paycheque. After my humbling experience today, I was even more so. I signed the back of my cheque and handed it to the teller. As she began to count, I pushed in a little closer and leaned right into the wicket so she wouldn't have to count so loud.

"Twenty, forty, sixty . . .," she began, ". . . and twenty-five, twenty-six, and twenty-seven cents." Her voice pierced my eardrums as she called out loud and clear every last cent to which I was entitled.

"Thanks," I muttered, grabbing my money and stuffing it into my pants pocket.

"Aren't you going to count your money?" she asked, looking a little surprised.

"You did that well enough for both of us," I replied.

I lowered my head as I bolted past the lineup and charged out into the street.

"How come you're home?" Mar asked when I made a surprise visit at the house.

"Come here," I said. "I want you to count this."

I took the money from my pocket and laid it on the table. I sat down and watched as she counted every cent.

"Well?" I said, looking her in the eye.

"Well, what?" she asked, somewhat bewildered.

"Well, what did you see?" I asked.

"Three hundred and fourteen dollars and twenty-seven cents," she replied.

"That's it? You don't see anything else?" I asked.

"That's it," she replied and spread the bills out on the table, giving them another going-over. "What else was I supposed to see?"

"Poverty!" I snorted. "We're living in poverty."

"I know," she said, unfazed by my marvellous revelation. "I've been telling you that since we got married."

THE OFFICE MIRROR

"A mountain district? For me? Yeah, right," I muttered to the Powers That Be. "I'd say that's a pretty sick joke."

My secretary was away, and I was sitting at her desk practising my typing skills when I received the phone call that would once again change my life.

"It's no joke, Adams," he said firmly. "We've decided to transfer you."

"To a mountain district?" I repeated. "Sure you have."

"For a guy who's constantly squawking about a mountain district, you don't sound very happy."

"Yeah, well, I guess I'm sorta getting used to the Old Folks' Home," I said as I stood up and looked across the room at the office mirror that ran the entire length of the wall. Automatically, I reached up with my free hand and straightened my tie, then I tugged at the corner of my tunic. "You know, after a while this place just grows on you."

He chuckled. "And I'm sure Hinton will grow on you, too. After all, it's practically in your old backyard."

"Hinton! But . . . but the Division doesn't even have an office in Hinton."

"We do now," he declared. "There's a brand-new office there, and it's just waiting for an ambitious young fellow. Just think, Adams, you'll be able to set it up exactly the way you want it."

Oh yes, I thought, a brand-new district and a brand-new office, you can set it up the way you want it. Now, where had I heard that before? Instantly, I had flashbacks. I could feel a knot growing and twisting in my stomach, the result of visions from similar words spoken four years earlier. Memories of events, like living nightmares, suddenly flooded my mind.

It had been the spring of '62 when my promotion and transfer to Strathmore had been announced. I could still remember the tingle of excitement and anticipation of great things to come. My own district, my own boss, my own office. Ah, yes, my own brand-new office. But my first spring in Strathmore did not produce an office. And spring dragged into summer. Summer wasted away to fall. Fall finally spun into winter. And winter brought me another spring. It had been a year, a long drawn-out miserable year of working out of my house, and I was still waiting for the brand-new office I had been promised when I was transferred to Strathmore.

"Hi there, it's me again," I said to the Powers That Be. "I, uh . . . that is . . ., well, actually, it's my wife, you see, she's pregnant and she's irritable and well, you know, she has these strange cravings. She wants all sorts of weird things, like mostly she wants her house to herself. She says she doesn't want to share it with the government anymore. You know what pregnant women are like, don't you?"

"I understand," he replied sympathetically. "You tell her that the office will come in good time."

"I've told her that for months now," I said. "I don't think she believes me anymore, and I was just wondering how the hunt for office space is coming along."

I had to admit that I was beginning to have grave doubts that Strathmore would ever see a real Fish and Wildlife Office. However, I was undeterred in my quest and I never passed up an opportunity to bug the Powers That Be. I used any little excuse as a reason to call them. Today was no exception.

"You tell your wife we're doing our best," he replied. By the tone of his voice, I thought he was genuinely sympathetic to our plight, until he added, "You know, Adams, Rome wasn't built in a day, and hounding me every single minute isn't helping your cause one bit."

"I know," I mumbled, "but you're a married man, and you know what women are like. For some strange reason, my wife thinks your office is her home. She's losing her patience. She really wants your office out of here. Can you believe, she reminds me every day that it's been close to a year now."

"Well, Adams, humour her a little," he said.

"Oh, I think I have been," I assured him. "You know, there was a time when she used to laugh at my humour, but not anymore. I think it's wearing a little thin. She even said that she'd like to be able to decorate her home, like a normal person. She went so far as to say she'd just be happy if she could see her kitchen table top."

"Adams, you have to clean up after yourself, you know. When you're finished working, take your work off the table. Pick up after yourself. My goodness, man, you young bucks can't even think for yourself anymore. Do I have to tell you everything?" he scolded.

"I tried cleaning off the table," I said, "but you know, she won't let me put any of my stuff in the living room, and there's only so many places in the kitchen. I tried putting it on the kitchen counter. That didn't work; it interfered with her work space. I even tried to commandeer a larger portion of the floor, where I've got most of the office supplies stacked. That was even worse—I've already got so much junk piled up there, she's tripping over it. Thanks to your office, I think I've just about worn my welcome out in my own home."

"You assure your good wife that I'm personally doing everything I can to get you an office," he told me. "In fact, I've had a man down there several times looking for office space. You say hello to your wife for me, and the next time you're in Edmonton, you bring her in with you. I'd like to see her again."

"I'll be sure to tell her what you said," I replied. "I'm sure she'll be as excited as all get-out."

The lack of an office in the Strathmore District was becoming a test of the strength of our marriage. I had a feeling that a few of the threads were coming unravelled. To my knowledge, no one had been in town looking for office space; if there had been, I felt confident that I would have heard. But I knew one person who would know for sure.

I was on my way to pick up a road-killed deer, when I met my buddy George.

"C'mon for a ride. I gotta pick up a road-killed deer, and I've got something to ask you," I said.

George got into my Forestry Green station wagon and as I drove away, I told him that the Powers That Be had sent someone to Strathmore looking for office space for me.

"I don't think so, boy," George said.

"Well, you know, George, I have it straight from the horse's mouth," I said. "The Powers That Be assured me that they've had a guy out looking for office space on several occasions now."

"I'm sure they did, but I think you've been listening to the wrong end of the horse," George said, and he laughed. That's what I liked about George, he could find humour in any situation. "They haven't been to Strathmore."

"Yeah, that's what I figured," I sighed. "You know, I gotta find me some office space, and yesterday wouldn't be too soon either."

"Getting a little crowded in the house, is it?" George asked with a laugh.

"You don't know the half of it," I replied. "Mar's got one of the bedrooms fixed up to be a nursery, and the other one looks like an armoury."

George looked at me and chuckled. "So what else is

new?" he said.

"The in-laws are coming and there's no room at the inn."

"There's lots of room at the motel." George said and laughed. I could always count on George to come up with an easy solution to a sticky problem. "I'd like to be there when you tell them they have to go to the motel." This was obviously a lot more humorous to George than it was to me.

We found the roadkill lying on the shoulder of the road. It was a small mule deer doe.

"What are you going to do with it?" George asked as we surveyed the carcass.

"I'm not sure," I replied. "We could give it to someone for dog feed, or I suppose take it to the dump."

"But that's good meat," George said. He was emphatic as he added, "You're not gonna throw away good meat, are you?"

"Yeah, I am, unless you know someone who wants it for their dog." I replied.

"That's a waste, boy," George declared. "Let's dress it out. We can get the butcher to cut it up and give it to some needy family. I know lots of people who could use some fresh meat."

" *You* can give it to the butcher," I told him. "The last time I took a roadkill in to have it cut up, it cost the butcher a saw blade when he hit a rock. I don't think I'm too popular around his place."

"We can do it," George proposed. "You and me. We can do it."

180

"Yeah, I suppose we could," I replied. "Now, all we gotta do is find a place to do it. Any suggestions?"

It was mid-afternoon when we arrived back at my place.

"What are you doing now?" Mar asked when George and I showed up at the back door with a deer carcass.

"We're gonna cut and wrap this deer," George warbled happily. I stood back and let George do the talking; he was on his own. "Then we're gonna give it to a needy family."

"You're not bringing that stinky thing into my kitchen," Mar stated firmly.

George never hesitated for a second; he just laughed and the words continued to roll off his tongue. "That's just the good smell of fresh meat! It shouldn't take too long. It's just a little job for old pros like us. We'll have this thing cut up and out of here in no time."

"I'm going for a walk." Mar sighed. She wasn't surprised; the deer was just another in a long line of inconveniences, and she had resigned herself to the inevitable. "You better have that thing out of my house by the time I get back."

"Walks are good for pregnant ladies," George said and laughed. "You won't even know we've been here when you get back."

George and I quickly found out what the butcher already knew: cutting up a road-killed deer was not as easy at it sounded. The broken, crushed bones were difficult to separate from the meat. That task was only slightly easier than trimming off all the bruised areas.

We almost needed tweezers to remove the dirt and gravel that had been ground into the flesh. There was still a large portion of the deer that lay untouched by the time Mar returned from her walk.

"Aren't you finished yet?" she asked.

"Just about," George replied. "It took a little longer than we thought to get the hang of it."

"Who's gonna eat that?" Mar asked. "I think I'm going to barf. That thing stinks to high heaven."

"That's just the smell of mule deer," I told her. "Mule deer are a bit stronger than other big-game animals. The meat will be fine."

"I wouldn't feed that thing to my dog," she declared.

"We don't have a dog," I reminded her.

"I've got to go to bed. I can't stand that smell. Why don't you turn on the lights?" she asked and flicked on the switch. "Maybe now you can see what you're doing." It was then I realized we had been at this little job most of the afternoon and all evening, and we still had a lot of trimming to do.

George and I never slowed down — we both wielded our knives, cutting, trimming, and picking. It was well past midnight when we hauled the scraps out the back door. George and I paused for a moment, each with our own thoughts, as we measured the fruits of our labour. Then I went to the cupboard; I took out a soup bowl and put it on the table. I tenderly picked up the meat we had salvaged, put it in the soup bowl, and covered it with wax paper. There was no need for further words. We both knew that this was absolutely the last time we would spend twelve hours on a roadkill.

A couple of days later, Mar was singing little ditties as she bustled around the house. She was as happy as a lark. Gone was the nausea from the smell of mule deer. For the first time in months, the sight of my office wasn't a concern. A new force, much stronger than these minor irritants, had entered our home. Her mother and father had arrived for the long-awaited visit.

Our house was the happiest of homes as Mar prepared and served supper. Not a cross word was spoken as the dishes were done. Once more, we settled ourselves around the table, this time for a marathon session of bridge. Finally, it was time for bed.

"If we're going to bed, I guess I better go and clean out the back bedroom," I said.

"It's okay," Mar replied happily. "I'm just going to make a bed on the floor in the living room."

"Just a minute. You can't ask your parents to sleep on the floor, and certainly not in the living room," I told Mar.

"I'm not," she said. "They're sleeping in our bed. We're sleeping on the floor."

"What do you mean, they're sleeping in our bed?" I objected. "That's my bed, let them sleep on that old bed in the spare bedroom."

"I'm not asking my Mom and Dad to sleep in that old bed. Anyway, there's no space in the spare bedroom, or on that old bed," she replied. "It's full of your Fish and Wildlife junk, remember?"

"Well, what about us, then? I'll move some of the

stuff around and we can sleep in the spare room then, can't we?"

"Have you been in there lately?" she asked. "There's guns leaning up against every wall. There's guns lying all over the floor. There's more junk and who-knows-what-all in there. I'm not sleeping in there with all those guns and that junk."

"But you're pregnant. You shouldn't be sleeping on the floor," I argued.

"I'll be fine," she replied. "Anyway, the floor is better than sleeping with all those guns."

"Well, I've got to go to work in the morning. I don't want to sleep on the floor."

"You better get your clothes out of Mom and Dad's bedroom if you want them for the morning," Mar said, totally ignoring me.

"Are you okay, boy?" George asked me a couple of days later when I was riding with him. "You don't seem to be yourself."

"I've got to get an office, George," I moaned. "The in-laws have taken over my bedroom, and Mar and I are sleeping on the floor. I don't know how she does it in her condition, but I know I've had a kink in my neck since they arrived, and now my back is killing me. It seems like every day someone has rearranged my office and my files. I can't find anything. My house is a mess. My office is a mess. I'm a mess."

When we arrived back in Strathmore, we were driving down the main drag when suddenly George wheeled his car into the curb and parked right in front of an old building. It was a store with two huge plate-glass windows full of goods for sale. It was one of those rare moments: George just sat there, not saying a word, staring into the windows in front of us. I sat there staring at George as if he had just lost his marbles.

"You know, boy," George said when he found his voice, "I heard a rumour that the guy who runs this business just might be looking for something else to do."

"Really?" I replied. "If you think he'll rent the building, I'm all for it. Right now, I'd take a barn if I could rent one."

"You never know," George said and laughed. "This could be it, it might just be your new office. This place has an interesting history. It wasn't always a store, you know. At one time it was a barbershop."

"Is that so?" Now I, too, was staring hopefully at the large plate-glass windows. "Sounds to me like it's exactly what I've been looking for, a versatile building."

"Let's go and talk to him, we'll see what he has to say," George said. "It can't do no harm, now, can it?"

We were barely through the door before George started talking.

I followed him in and while he talked, told jokes, and laughed, I listened, nodded my head, and surveyed the inside of the building. Man, I thought, you're wasting your time, George; this place is huge, it's way too big. I had been in a few Fish and Wildlife offices and had a pretty good idea of how much space was needed. I figured there was enough room in this place for four or five offices, maybe even six. It definitely had potential, but deep inside I knew there was absolutely no way the Powers That Be would ever approve something this large for a Fish and Wildlife office. George was undaunted; he was talking, joking, and laughing. Once more, I stood back and listened. I learned long ago that it was far wiser to let George talk. And he talked.

"Hi, it's me again," I said to the Powers That Be when I made my daily phone call. My greeting was met with the usual wall of silence. "Guess what?" I continued.

"What now?" came the curt response.

"I found an office!" I said. There was a really long, pregnant pause. "Hello. Hello? Are you still there? Did you hear me? I said I found an office. Well, actually, it was George, he found it for me."

"I see, well, if that's true, then I guess that would be good news, wouldn't it," he finally replied.

"No, that would be *great* news," I assured him. "In fact, Mar has already started to reclaim her house, she's packing up all the Division's junk as we speak."

"Yes, I'm sure she is," he muttered. "I'm sure she is."

"You know," I told him, "had it not been for my good friend George, I doubt there ever would have been a Fish and Wildlife Office in Strathmore."

"I'll see to it that we get someone on it right away," he said.

I could hardly believe it when the truck pulled up in front of the brand-new Fish and Wildlife Office in Strathmore. It was even harder to believe when they started unloading the furniture. There was a counter, complete with a locking drawer — a safe place to keep the licences and cash. There was a bench to place right in front of one of the huge plate-glass windows. Six chairs were hauled in and lined up in front of the other plate-glass window. A steno's desk and chair were placed just behind the counter. Another desk and chair were hauled into my private office. And then a third desk was brought in and placed in the huge open area where the six chairs had been placed. I couldn't believe the windfall as more furniture walked through the door, a filing cabinet and bookshelf. And if that wasn't good enough, I even got some file baskets and not one, but *two* garbage buckets.

It didn't take me long to arrange all the furniture. Next I placed my personal items neatly on my desk. After I had stuffed the drawers with office materials I was a little short of space for some of the files. I looked around the room. There was ample space, so I walked over to one corner and dropped them on the floor.

"Does that offend anyone?" I called out, and my voice echoed throughout the office.

In no time flat, I was ready for business. In less time than it took me to arrange the furniture, I realized that I was lord and master of what had to be the biggest Fish and Wildlife office in Alberta. This place was immense. Yes, I thought, at least the Powers That Be knew what they were doing when they sent me furniture. At first, I thought I had too many desks, too much furniture, but that was not so. Once it was properly arranged, I found I had the right amount of furniture.

I sat at my desk, in my private office, and surveyed my kingdom. Man, but my office was a grand place.

"Can you bring me the court docket," I called out to my non-existent secretary.

Then I arose from behind my desk and strode out to the secretary's desk. I plunked my butt down in the secretary's chair and hammered out a few lines on the typewriter. Then I reached over and picked the court docket out of the file basket marked "Court" and returned to my office.

"Your court docket, sir," purred the phantom secretary.

"Thank you kindly," I replied. Then I checked each file, the Informations, the affidavits of seizures, and the exhibit reports. I confirmed that each case had been set for court the following Monday.

"Is everything in order?" asked the phantom secretary when I walked into the main office and dropped the docket on the office's third desk.

"Absolutely," I replied and chuckled. "As usual, everything is A-1." Once more I walked over and plunked myself down behind the secretary's desk. I looked back at the docket lying there out of place on that desk, but no one told me to take it and put it back where it belonged. Ah, yes, it was indeed a great feeling to have an office.

For the moment, I sat in the secretary's chair, behind the secretary's desk, and slowly surveyed my kingdom. The east wall of my office was covered with huge mirrors, and glass shelves, remnants of the old barbershop, reminders of the building's interesting past. The mirrors provided greater depth and gave my office a much larger look. Those shelves will be perfect to display some of the wildlife species found in the district, I was thinking, and then I spotted him. I took a second look, and he looked back. When I smiled, he smiled back. Then I stood up and I straightened out my pea-green tie. My tunic had ridden up when I was arranging the furniture, and I tugged at the corners until it lay properly. I stood there admiring the sharp-looking dude in full uniform. Ah, yes, I chuckled to myself, I've only been in here for one day and already I love it. My brand-new office with the old barber's mirrors was indeed a grand place.

*   *   *

It seemed like only yesterday, but three years had flown by since I had moved into the Strathmore Fish and Wildlife Office. Now, once more, the Powers That Be were advising me that I was on the move. This time, Mar and I were not alone; we now had two little girls. I hung up the phone and stood there looking at the office mirror and the glass shelves, which were now lined with mounted birds.

"Why do I get this feeling that Mar will not be thrilled when I tell her I'm getting a brand-new office in a brand-new mountain district?" I asked the guy in the office mirror. Then I stood up tall and straight. I picked up my hat and placed it on my head. I straightened out my tunic and smiled. The guy in the mirror smiled back. I'm going to miss this old barbershop, I thought, as I strode out to break the news to Mar.

189

ROBERT J. (BOB) ADAMS

Bob Adams was born in Turner Valley, Alberta in 1938. He grew up in the Edson area, in a log house, built by his father on a farm rich in swamp spruce, tamarack, willows and muskeg.

Bob, an avid outdoorsman, was one of the fortunate few who was able to live his boyhood dreams as he entered the workforce. In 1960, after a number of years with the Alberta Forest Service and Royal Canadian Mounted Police, he began a career with the Provincial Government as a Fish and Wildlife Officer. For the next 33 years, he found his homes to include Brooks, Strathmore, Hinton, Calgary, Peace River and Edmonton.

In 1993, after a full career in Enforcement, he retired from Fish and Wildlife and wrote his first book, The Stump Farm. Today, Bob resides in Edmonton, Alberta with his wife Martha where he continues to work on his writing.

GIVE A "ROBERT J. ADAMS" BOOK TO A FRIEND

Megamy Publishing Ltd.
Box 3507
Spruce Grove, AB   T7X 3A7

Send to:
Name:_____

Street:_____

City:_____
Province/   Postal/
State:_____ Zip Code:_____

Please send:

"The Stump Farm"   @ $16.95 = _____

"Beyond the Stump Farm"   @ $16.95 = _____

"Horse Cop"   @ $16.95 = _____

"Fish Cop"   @ $16.95 = _____

"The Elephant's Trunk"   @ $15.95 = _____

"The South Road"   @ $16.95 = _____

"Skunks and Hound Dogs"   @ $16.95 = _____

Shipping and handling per book   @ $ 4.00 = _____

7% GST   = _____

Total amount enclosed: _____

Make cheque or money order payable to:
Megamy Publishing Ltd.
Price subject to change without prior notice.
ORDERS OUTSIDE OF CANADA must be paid in U.S. funds by
cheque or money order drawn on U.S. or Canadian Bank.
Sorry no C.O.D.'s.